WESTMAR COLLEGE LIBRARY

D1241316

THE *JULIUS EXCLUSUS* OF ERASMUS

The
Julius exclusus
of
Erasmus

Translated by Paul Pascal

Introduction and Critical Notes
by J. KELLEY SOWARDS

Indiana University Press
BLOOMINGTON · LONDON

262.13
E65

BX
1314
·E713

COPYRIGHT © 1968 BY INDIANA UNIVERSITY PRESS
ALL RIGHTS RESERVED

*No part of this book may be reproduced or utilized in any
form or by any means, electronic or mechanical, including
photocopying and recording, or by any information storage
and retrieval system, without permission in writing from
the publisher. The Association of American University
Presses' Resolution on Permissions constitutes the only
exception to this prohibition.*

LIBRARY OF CONGRESS CATALOG NUMBER: 68-14600
MANUFACTURED IN THE UNITED STATES OF AMERICA

71906

Contents

Introduction

THE *Julius exclusus*
AND THE AUTHORSHIP QUESTION[1]

In the early months of the year 1517[2] appeared the first printed edition of a scurrilous, witty, wicked and anonymous dialogue attacking the late Pope Julius II. Julius had died some four years before but his memory was very much alive. The mounting clamor of anti-papal criticism, which was soon to swell into the Protestant Reformation, had long since taken this war-like pope as the very image of diabolical Anti-Christ. The dialogue—while it appeared under many variant titles in its earliest editions—is best known as *Julius exclusus*. It posed the shade of the dead pope, accompanied by his guiding genius and his stinking, motley army, at heaven's gates demanding admittance of St. Peter. In its course, as we shall see, the pope was flayed for his bellicose temporal policies, the sins and crimes of his private life, the corruption of his court, and his all too obvious contrast to the apostolic ideal embodied in St. Peter, the dialogue's other principal character.

In the next few months copies and editions of this little book appeared in Cologne, in Basel, in Paris, in Louvain and Antwerp. It was reported in a dozen other places and read all over Europe.

It seemed to be everywhere and to come from nowhere. The early editions are almost impossible either to trace or to identify.[3] Any number of them may have disappeared without a trace, for this book was part of the enormous glut of pamphlet literature which was a staple of the popular press in the early sixteenth century—cheaply and hastily printed, usually slanderous, often anonymous and often pirated by one printer from another.

The reaction to the Julius dialogue was immediate, loud, and varied. Most of the liberal humanists were delighted. The pious and conventional were properly shocked. The right-wing, ortho-dox defenders of the ecclesiastical status quo were furious. The Cologne theologians, still smarting from the first assault of *The Letters of Obscure Men,* attacked the book savagely.[4] The conservative young theologian Martin van Dorp wrote to his friend Erasmus from Louvain:

> Everyone here is reading the little book on Pope Julius excluded from heaven—and it is strange how few condemn it—: although you would be annoyed at the author, with good reason, who makes literature suspect at this time.[5]

Guy Morillon, a humanist of the Burgundian court circle, wrote to Erasmus from Brussels that everyone there was laughing over it.[6] And Erasmus reported to Thomas More that even the Burgundian chancellor Jean Le Sauvage was immensely pleased with it.[7] Peter Giles, the municipal secretary of Antwerp, wrote to Erasmus:

> The Julius dialogue—by whom I don't know, but certainly a learned man—is for sale everywhere here: everyone is buying it and it is on everyone's lips. I surely wish you had seen it; although it is doubtless for sale there.[8]

Indeed it was.

But who was its author?

By some it was attributed to a nameless Spaniard residing in Paris.[9] Others thought it was a Latin translation of a popular

Parisian court jest.[10] A great many people, including the Bishop of Paris,[11] credited it to Faustus Andrelinus, the Italian humanist expatriate and sometime French court poet. And with good reason. He had the wit for it and it was precisely the sort of irreverent prank for which he had a long reputation. Most of all, the work had something of a pro-French bias and, in his capacity as court poet, Faustus was an outspoken apologist for French royal policy.[12]

On the basis of the book's anti-papal temper and in the context of recent politics, there was equally good reason to attribute it to a German or pro-German writer. Some assigned it to Girolamo Balbi[13] and he was indeed a likely "suspect." Like Faustus he was an Italian humanist adventurer. He had spent some time in Paris in Faustus' company but his impertinent writings, personal quarrels and vicious habits had dictated a somewhat migratory habit which took him from one court, or university, or city to another. He had finally attached himself to Matthias Lang, the German Bishop of Gurk and the belligerent personal representative of the Emperor Maximilian in most of his dealings with Pope Julius II. Moreover, Balbi at about this time had succeeded to Lang's bishopric and presumably to his sycophant's role at the imperial court.[14] But most of those who held the "German view" of the *Julius'* authorship attributed it, naturally enough, to the pen of Ulrich von Hutten. Hutten's ultranationalism and violent secular opinions had already led him to attack the papacy in a series of intemperate epigrams.[15]

But from the very first a considerable and perceptive body of opinion had favored Erasmus as the author of the dialogue. In the same letter in which he reported the book's happy reception at the court of Burgundy, Guy Morillon called it "so charming, so witty," and—with a shameless verbal wink—"in a word, so Erasmian"![16] Others, as we have seen, were not so amused. Some Cologne theologians were already accusing Erasmus of the writing. In a series of letters which he was reasonably sure would

9

receive wide circulation, Erasmus indignantly protested the charge, pointing to several others who had better cause to write it; denying its affinity with *The Praise of Folly;* and ridiculing the weakness of an argument from style:—"[my informant] tells me something even I can scarcely believe, that many suspect me of writing it because the Latin 'isn't so bad!' "[17]

But the charge remained and the theologians fumed.

On January 1, 1519, Erasmus wrote to his friend Thomas More from Louvain:

> Will these slanderers never stop? They leave no stone unturned to do harm to Erasmus! They've convinced many people in Cologne that that outrageous little book . . . was written by me; and they would have convinced many more if I had not promptly blunted the edge of their treacherous lies.[18]

Some months later he took the trouble to write to the English Cardinal Wolsey and the Cardinal-Legate Campeggio what may be called a full-dress denial of the accusation. He rehearsed his earlier arguments; said he had not written the dialogue; and indeed had scarcely even read it:

> . . . my detractors try to throw upon me the suspicion for a certain dialogue. As is evident from the argument, they say it was written to cast odium upon the blessed Pope Julius in the time of the schism: but by whom it is not known. Some five years ago I did read it—or more properly, glanced at it. Afterwards I came across it again in Germany appearing in the works of several people and under various titles.[19]

At about the same time, the ever-faithful More took up the cause of his beleaguered friend. In his classic defence of Erasmus' Greek New Testament—the famous letter "To a Monk"—More turned aside long enough to defend Erasmus' position on the *Julius* question. His arguments were essentially the same as Erasmus had already used but More argued them like the skillful lawyer he was, leaning on the strong points, sliding over the weak ones, clouding the issue with ridicule of the charge and the accusers.[20]

Yet even as More argued against the charge that Erasmus had written the *Julius,* he had intimate and certain knowledge that his friend *had* written it!

Some five or six years before, in the summer of 1514, Erasmus had left England for the continent after a long stay at Cambridge and in London. With his usual haste and impatience he had left a number of things behind, including several manuscripts in various stages of completion or revision. He had apparently instructed his trusted young Cambridge secretary, Thomas Lupset, to collect this material and get it to him. As the months stretched into a year and then a year and a half, Erasmus made insistent inquiries about his belongings to Lupset and to other English friends.[21] His concern was clearly more than his usual suspicion of what nefarious use others might be making of his work.[22] And this is borne out by the very circumspect letter that Lupset finally wrote to him in June of 1516. In it he protests his good faith and, after lengthy apology and explanation, adds:

> The things of yours that I kept I would have turned over to Peter [the courier who conveyed many of Erasmus' letters and packets] if I hadn't felt that it was safer to keep them until your own return. Therefore, when you return, I shall give them to you complete and, believe me, intact.[23]

Instead he turned them over to More, who informed Erasmus:

> Lupset has returned to me several of your manuscripts which he's had. Among them is "Iulii Genius," and two declamations . . . ; all of them in your hand, but the former is little more than a scribble, a fragment.[24]

As Wallace K. Ferguson has pointed out:

> The "Iulii Genius" clearly refers to the dialogue, a rough draft in the author's autograph. Erasmus was far too busy, and made

too much use of secretaries, to have copied out so long a work
by some one else; nor in that case would it have been in the incomplete state described by More.[25]

Two or three months later, on March 1, 1517, in another letter
to More, Erasmus ended with these instructions, "Send me back
copies of the letters I am sending you now as well as the things
that Lupset returned—but in the hands of a 'safe' man."[26]

There was, moreover, at least one other manuscript copy—
possibly more[27]—and one of them found its way into the hands
of some "not so safe" man. For this was apparently how the
Julius came into print, without either the knowledge or consent
of Erasmus. It is probable that he never intended to publish it
himself. Yet even as he finally recovered the copy he had left with
Lupset, the early printed editions were beginning to appear.[28]
He had evidently taken with him to the continent another draft
of the book and possibly allowed his friends in Basel to hand it
around as he had allowed his friends in England to do. It was
copied by Boniface Amerbach—which copy still exists—and, as
P. S. Allen asserts, "it is quite clear that the *Iulius* must have been
known to Erasmus' intimate friends at Basel as early as August
1516."[29] We cannot be sure that this was the copy that "escaped"
and Erasmus seems to have attached no blame to Amerbach.
There were simply too many people in on the secret and someone
had given a copy—either carelessly or intentionally—to a printer.
Once the book was in print, as we have seen, the printings and
editions multiplied until, within months, it was known all over
Europe.[30]

The existence of these incriminating manuscripts was not
widely known and the few who knew about them were unusually
discreet. Erasmus' friends joined him in suggesting other likely
authors for the piece and in discrediting the suggestion that he
had written it: his enemies were never able to prove conclusively
that he had.

This satiric book continued to cause occasional comment. As late as the summer of 1521, Erasmus wrote to Richard Pace:

> Even now they accuse me of the little Julius-book. There is nothing they won't do to injure me—not really me so much as good learning which they have no wish to see flourish.[31]

There have remained those who "accuse" him as the debate on "the little Julius-book" continued into modern critical scholarship.[32]

In a general way it is obvious why Erasmus would have been reluctant to claim the book. But that he should have gone to such lengths to deny it[33] runs counter to the strong and somewhat childish streak of pride that he was apt to display, often at the most inopportune moments. He had, after all, published as trenchant a satire as *The Praise of Folly* and acknowledged it. Yet he himself saw clearly the difference between the *Folly* and the *Julius*. In one of his several letters denying the authorship of the *Julius* he wrote:

> It is true that I "played the fool" in the *Folly*—but bloodlessly! I have never injured the reputation of anyone by name. I have satirized the *mores* of men, not their reputations.[34]

This he could no longer claim if he acknowledged the *Julius*.

But more than a piece of his literary reputation was at stake. From the very pope whom he had just condemned so roundly Erasmus had himself received, some ten years before, a valuable dispensation absolving him from the disabilities of his illegitimacy (thus enabling him to hold church benefices) and freeing him of his ties with the hated monastery of Steyn.[35] Moreover, at the very time the *Julius* dialogue appeared in print, Erasmus was carrying on a complicated negotiation with Leo X, Julius' successor, to have the terms of the earlier dispensation confirmed and extended.[36] Under the circumstances, even his most ardent champions would have to admit that this was an awkward time to bite the papal hand.

Perhaps an even more important factor was his need for Leo's help in the most serious enterprise he had yet undertaken. As Ferguson states it:

> His Greek New Testament had just been published under the patronage of the new Pope. In the long war which followed with the obscurantists at Louvain and Cologne he needed Leo's support; and as the Lutheran movement developed, his position became sufficiently difficult without his having to answer for so virulent an attack on the papacy.[37]

Thus, more pressing and practical considerations overcame the pull of the powerful Erasmian ego and he never publicly claimed his raffish intellectual offspring

THE MAKING OF THE *Julius*

The *Julius exclusus* was probably written shortly after the death of the pope in 1513 or 1514,[38] while Erasmus was at Cambridge. The five or six preceding years are, unfortunately, the most obscure and poorly documented period in the mature life of Erasmus[39]—the very years during which the events of his life were preparing the way for the *Julius.*

In 1506 he had finally gotten his chance to go to Italy, the pilgrimage goal of every northern scholar, home of the New Learning, "where the walls are more learned and eloquent than our men"![40] To his surprise and delight he was welcomed everywhere in Italy and showered with honors. In Turin, Bologna, and Florence scholars took him in, libraries opened their doors to him, and he was accepted by the salons and learned societies of Rome and Venice.[41] This visit to Italy became the watershed of Erasmus' career. His youth was over, the years of obscurity and struggle and arduous apprenticeship were past.[42] He was prepared to return to the north and become the Prince of Humanists. But Italy also completed the preparation of Erasmus as the Prince of Satirists. For he had seen not only the glamor, the books, the printing-houses, the cordial scholars and graceful patrons of Italy: he had seen also the cynicism, venality, and wholesale corruption of the Italian clergy; and, most shocking of all, he had come face to face with the brutal secularism of the papacy in the person of Julius II.[43]

Shortly after his arrival in Italy Erasmus had settled in the city of Bologna for a comfortable and productive winter—only to be chased out by the pope's warlike preparations against Bologna.[44] He returned in time to witness, if not the fall of the city, at least the ceremonial entry of the pope—"warring, conquering, triumphing, acting the very Julius!"[45]

Within a few months Erasmus accepted the hospitality of the famous Venetian printer Aldus Manutius and threw himself into the work of revising and vastly expanding his *Adagia*.[46] But the specter of Julius was never far out of mind for, at this very time, the pope was directing all his ferocious enmity against Venice and the Venetian threat to his north Italian ambitions. Leaving Venice in the mid-winter of 1508, Erasmus stopped at Padua planning to stay some months. But once more the threat of war forced him to move on.[47] In December of 1508 the League of Cambrai was formed. By the following spring the pope had joined it and the towns of northern Italy, including Padua, found themselves the battleground and the prizes of war. The participation of the pope, barely defensible to the dispassionate modern historian, was nothing less than monstrous to Erasmus who, with some lack of charity, saw Julius as the prime mover of the league.[48]

In the later winter or early spring of 1509, Erasmus finally visited Rome.[49] He was entertained by some of the highest officials of the papal court—with whom he later boasted intimacy.[50]

Perhaps he was received by Julius.[51] But in Rome, least of all, could he escape the corrosive influence of papal secularism. And he blamed Julius. Some years later he recalled an instructive incident:

> When I was in Rome, on the request of Raphael Cardinal St. George, who approached me in the name of Julius, I composed an oration against the proposition of undertaking a war against Venice—at the time this was under consideration in the College of Cardinals. Then I composed one *for* the same proposition. The latter oration was the winner although I had worked harder on the former.[52]

His visit to Rome was cut short by the invitation from Lord Mountjoy and Archbishop Warham to return to England and the "mountains of gold" which the reign of the new, young king Henry VIII seemed to promise.[53] As he traveled north once more, the thoughts of Italy went with him and in the course of the long and tiresome journey these thoughts joined with those of the good and virtuous friends he was shortly to see once more in England. The product of this rumination was the famous *Praise of Folly,* completed after Erasmus' arrival in England and dedicated to his friend Thomas More.[54]

The impressions of Italy formed a bundle of the most important themes in *The Praise of Folly,* and none was more important than the papacy—specifically the papacy of Julius II. Of whom but Julius could Erasmus have been thinking when he made his foolish goddess say:

> Who would purchase that office at the cost of every effort? Who would retain it by the sword, by poison, and by every other way? If wisdom should come to Popes, what comforts it would deprive them of! Did I say wisdom? Even that grain of sense which Christ speaks of would do it. It would deprive them of all wealth, honor, and possessions; all the triumphal progresses, offices, dispensations, tributes, and indulgences; the many horses,

mules, and retainers; in short, it would deprive them of all their pleasures.[55]

More pointedly:

> The Popes are sufficiently generous with . . . interdictions, excommunications, re-excommunications, anathematizations, pictured damnations, and the terrible bolt of the papal bull, which by a flicker hurls the souls of men to the depths of hell. Our Christian fathers and vicars of Christ wield the bolt against no one with more zeal than against those who are moved by the devil to nibble at and diminish the patrimony of Peter. He said, "We have forsaken all, and followed Thee"; yet they give the name of patrimony to lands, towns, tributes, taxes, and riches. They fight for these things with fire and sword, inflamed by Christian zeal, and not without shedding Christian blood. They look on themselves as true apostles, defending the bride of Christ, and scattering what they are pleased to call her enemies. As if the church had more deadly enemies than impious popes who by their silence cause Christ to be forgotten, who use His laws to make money, who adulterate His word with forced interpretations, and who crucify Him with their corrupt life![56]

And more pointedly still:

> War is so monstrous a thing that it befits beasts and not men, so violently insane that poets represent it as an evil visitation of the Furies, so pestilential that it causes a general corruption of character, so criminal that it is best waged by the worst of men, and so impious that it has no relation with Christ. Nevertheless, our popes neglect every thing else to devote themselves to war. Here you can see tired old men act with youthful energy and disregard all labor and expense, simply in order to overturn laws, religion, peace, and humane institutions.[57]

Thus transparently disguised, Pope Julius II took his place in the train of Folly!

The months that followed the composition of *The Praise of Folly* were furiously busy for Erasmus. He had several projects

17

in hand:[58] he was much occupied in trying to gain access to that lavish patronage for which he had specifically returned to England: and he was concerned to find suitable lodgings for what he hoped would be a long and comfortable stay.[59]

Yet, in the midst of all this activity, there must have been much visiting with those congenial London friends he loved so well and of whom he said, for learning not even Italy contained their like.[60] And there was talk, talk, and more talk—witty, urbane, and sparkling talk, punning, playing with words because they loved words; and serious and satiric talk because they loved truth and ideas equally well. Such talk must have turned often to Italy and the disgrace of Julius, for such he surely appeared to these serious-minded Englishmen, fully as much as to Erasmus.

Yet with all the good will of his scholar friends, Erasmus' personal fortunes did not materially improve. In the summer or fall of 1511—presumably when he had exhausted every other hope of patronage—he was finally constrained to accept a lectureship at Cambridge offered him by John Fisher, Bishop of Rochester.[61] Perhaps before leaving London, perhaps after his arrival at Cambridge he wrote the following satiric epigram:

AN EPIGRAM OF ERASMUS
AGAINST JULIUS II

1 Your name suits you perfectly,
   For you are certainly another Caesar.
   He was once even Supreme Pontiff.
   He unjustly seized tyrannical power, and
5 Had no greater compunction than do you
   About breaking his plighted word for
                   "reasons of state."
   He despised the gods: and are you
   Not a Julius in this respect?
   He turned the whole world upside down
   In slaughter, war, and blood: and
   Are you not another Julius in this?

10 He was the mighty harrier of the Gauls
    And are you not their very "pox"?
There was nothing sacred about him
    Except his sickness.
In his breast he held the vengeful Erinyes,
    Who drove him with Furies
As did his evil conscience.
15 The glance from his front was keen and menacing.
    And he was craftier than any stage-player:
Both in these and in other qualities
    Not to be ignored, you resemble, equal,—nay
Surpass the other Julius.
    You differ from him only in one
20 Tiny detail that, being of common stock,
    You love wine more than literature.
There remains only one thing to make
    You completely like Caesar:—
That you find some Brutus.
    One Nicomedes is not enough for you
Even though you are an old man.
    In this one regard, at least, you are more
        than Julius.[62]

This epigram is one of the most important links in the argument for Erasmus' authorship of the *Julius exclusus,* for in timing, theme, and treatment it clearly anticipates the longer and more elaborate satire.[63] Like the *Julius* it was never claimed by Erasmus and was not published in his lifetime. Indeed it was brought to light only about a generation ago by the French scholar J. B. Pineau who, on a suggestion of P. S. Allen, discovered it in a manuscript copy in Erasmus' own hand.[64] And to strengthen the case, on the reverse side of the manuscript is the name of Erasmus' friend Thomas More in the cryptic phrase, "Th. Morus Byth. Capad."[65]

Then in 1957 another manuscript copy of the epigram was discovered, inserted in a copy of a seventeenth century edition of the *Praise of Folly*. It has been described by the Dutch scholar Cornelis Reedijk as clearly contemporary—the watermark in the paper locates it—indisputably in the hand of Erasmus, and, in this case, with the scribbled name "Rosso" on the back of the manuscript, a pseudonym that More is known to have used. In addition to the name "Rosso" are several abbreviated words including, as in the earlier manuscript, what are apparently the abbreviations for the ancient provinces of Cappadocia and Bithynia, as well as Galatia and others. This is the same list of places to which the first letter of Peter in the New Testament was sent. And Reedijk has speculated that the author was already playing with the idea of the contrast between St. Peter and Julius II.[66] This stinging little epigram is the very sort of thing that Erasmus might have dashed off for the amusement of his English friends. But what is more important, it demonstrates Erasmus' bitter preoccupation with the anti-Julian theme in these same years.

During his stay at Cambridge this preoccupation is more easily documented in the considerable volume of letters, especially those exchanged with the Italian Andrea Ammonio. For Erasmus the drudgery of academic routine in a provincial university was bad enough at best. His lectures were poorly attended.[67] He was constantly bickering with the "Thomists and Scotists."[68] The periodic visitations of the plague came and went and he wrote Ammonio, "There is a great solitude here, most people away for fear of the plague, though when all are here it is still a solitude."[69] As often as he could he slipped away to London, but his health, his work, his poverty, and the plague kept him away from the city for months at a time.[70] He missed the company of his friends and the comforts of the city but as much as anything else he missed the news and gossip of London—especially news from the continent. In September 1511, at the end of a short note to Ammonio, he jotted, "I hear Julius Maximus is dead!"[71] But the rumor was false. On October 5, he inquired, "Is there any news of Italy and France that can be trusted to letters?":[72] and a week or so later, ". . . what's going on in Italy? What is the 'unconquerable Julius' up to?"[73] From London, Ammonio faithfully transmitted what he knew, and in his Italian friend Erasmus had an excellent source of information. He was the intimate of Silvestro de Gigli, the Bishop of Worcester, and a papal agent in England;[74] he himself had connections in Rome;[75] and, as a client and Latin Secretary to Lord Mountjoy and later to the king, he had access to the rumors and gossip of the court.[76] His letters to Erasmus read like news briefs. On October 27, he wrote:

> On the affairs of Italy these are the facts we have. Spain is nearly at the point of open war with France and, if it comes, the English will not be merely spectators, as one might well guess. "Julius Maximus" has betaken himself to the Church of Deipara in Loretto to give thanks to the saint for the restoration of his health. The Venetians, so they say, wiped out more than five hundred French cavalry in ambush. The emperor is so strapped that he does not dare issue forth from Germany. The Pisans and Florentines have let themselves in for considerable ill will because they support those schismatic cardinals in their council. The Cardinal of Rhegio has died.[77]

Ten days later another report:

> But to turn to Italian affairs: the Holy League has been formed between the Pope, the King of Spain, and the Venetians under the following terms: the King of Spain will supply to the Pope 1200 heavy cavalry (called lancers), 1000 light armored, and 10,000 infantry. The Pope will maintain 500 heavy cavalry and 8,000 infantry. In addition he will furnish 40,000 in gold per month for the hiring of mercenaries. The Venetians are collecting whatever forces they can. The Council of Pisa is off to a bad start. It is reported that the Cardinal of Santa Croce, the author of the schism, has received pardon from the Pope through the intervention of the King of Aragon and has hurried away to the

Campania. Oh, I forgot to mention, any Christian prince may join the League within forty days; after that they may be admitted at the will of the Pope. What our decision will be, I dare say, . . . hasn't yet been determined. The emperor will be only a spectator in this matter. Rumor has it that the Florentines are preparing to defect from the French.[78]

In his reply to these Erasmus writes:

What did you say? The Pope went to Loretto—what sterling piety! On the matter of the war that is just now breaking out isn't the Greek proverb appropriate, *the fate of the moth?* For surely if any misfortune should befall the Roman Church, I ask you, who would be more justly to blame than Julius "the over-strong"? But pray, even if you imagine the French driven out of Italy, would you prefer to have the Spanish as masters? Or the Venetians, scarcely tolerable to their own subjects? For princes will never endure *priests;* nor, moreover, is it likely they will compose their own differences for factional disputes are more insoluble than major disagreements. I fear that Italy will simply change masters.[79]

In November 1511, Ammonio writes again:

We have received letters from Italy, from which we learn that the French party is still the stronger; and that, in comparison, the Spanish are few, starved, and shoeless; that the Council of Pisa is proceeding; that the Cardinals of Santa Croce, of Cosenza, of Bayeaux, and of Narbonne have been degraded in public session and stripped of all their priestly prerogatives; finally, that famine, pestilence, slaughter, and rapine have exacted from the people of Bologna the well deserved rewards of treachery. So much from Italy.[80]

In mid-winter Erasmus heard, from his friend Paolo Bombace from Bologna, more of the pope's renewed attack on that city:[81] and in the spring of 1512, from Bombace, that in his city "nothing is to be seen but sorrow and confusion!"[82]

In the meantime another petty, personal grievance had been added to Erasmus' growing catalog of the sins of Julius. The pope had sent out a call for the Fifth Lateran Council. Erasmus' friend and patron Bishop Fisher had been commissioned to go from England and he had invited Erasmus to accompany him. What an opportunity to shake loose from his dreary life at Cambridge, to return to Rome with a brilliant company for a great church meeting for which he must have had high hopes of reform! But Julius postponed the opening of the council: Erasmus' opportunity was gone and he saw no good reason for it except the pope's perversity and a desire further to damage the cause of the church and reform.[83]

It was back to Cambridge once more. In May 1512, another letter to Ammonio:

> If you have any good rumors, please send them on to us. For I am most curious to hear whether Julius is still playing Caesar. . . .[84]

Then, through the summer and fall of 1512, there is no more correspondence with Ammonio, no more rumors, no more gossip of Julius and Italy. There is no letter to report that in the night of February 20-21, 1513, "Julius Maximus" died at last—no mistake this time—and none to report Erasmus' reaction to the news. But the result was the *Julius exclusus,* written almost certainly at this time, cautiously shown about, and finally escaping into print some three years later.

THE IMPORTANCE OF THE *Julius exclusus*

The fact that Erasmus wrote the *Julius exclusus* is sufficient to make it a literary curiosity and give to it a certain historical importance. But beyond curiosity it has a substantive value of its own as a work of literature and as a significant milestone in the career of the most celebrated literary figure of his generation. The *Julius exclusus* is a work of Erasmian satire second only to the famous *Praise of Folly*. Like the *Praise of Folly,* indeed like every work of satire however comic, its purpose was deadly serious: no less than the moral-religious reform of society. And like the *Praise of Folly* the *Julius exclusus* was a work of reflection and maturity, the product of Erasmus' own ideas of reform.

In 1501, when he was in his early thirties, Erasmus had written the *Enchiridion Militis Christiani,* his first major work of moral philosophy.[85] Three or four years later he edited and published the *Adnotationes* on the New Testament of the Italian humanist Lorenzo Valla, the first clear anticipation of his own great editorial project of the *Novum Instrumentum*.[86] Erasmus' visit to Italy had contributed significantly to his growing commitment to Christian humanism. There he perfected the tools of his literary craft and established his reputation as a scholar. But perhaps most significant of all, he had come at last to reject the spirit of Italian humanism in favor of the decision to return to the north.[87]

In England once more, the serious moral-reforming spirit of his English friends exerted a powerful influence upon Erasmus and tended to confirm the direction his own interests had already begun to take. He was still the scholar and humanist. He still edited Greek and Latin classic texts[88] and wrote books of rhetoric and grammar.[89] But, at the same time, he was already beginning to collect the materials and ponder the form of his works on the New Testament and the letters of St. Jerome.[90] The writings of these years are the documents of an inner purpose becoming increasingly clear and maturing into what Erasmus was to call his "philosophy of Christ."[91] The *Julius* must be seen in the light of this "philosophy" and in terms of the obvious and painful contrast between the ideal thus represented and the actuality of contemporary religious life. The contrast was as obvious to Erasmus as to us who look back to the early sixteenth century with the dispassion of historical perspective, and much more disquieting. From this disquiet grew the *Julius* as well as his other satirical works. For this is the mainspring of the Erasmian genius for satire. No more than implied in the wit and charm, the insight and astringency of his early works,[92] this gift becomes more apparent in the Aldine edition of the *Adagia*.[93] The first great document of Erasmian satire was *The Praise of Folly*. Certainly the second was the *Julius exclusus*.

The specific literary form that the *Julius exclusus* finally took may have reflected the influence of many contemporary writings. Bits and pieces of the work may have been suggested from a hundred sources, for the career of Julius II had caused anti-papal diatribe to blossom everywhere. Erasmus had seen it in its most frivolous and impromptu form in the Roman pasquinades. At about the time he visited Rome it was becoming customary for anonymous satirists to pin their epigrams and bits of doggerel to an ancient, mutilated statue which had been unearthed, set up, and given the name Pasquino. There was no mystery too sacred and no person too exalted for Pasquino's lampoons, not even the pope. Erasmus must have seen such pieces and may even have tried his hand at them. His anti-Julian epigram is certainly of this type.[94]

But while the pope had his sniping critics in Rome, Venice was the center of hard-core anti-papal propaganda in Italy. In the months that Erasmus spent in Venice he could scarcely have escaped the "constant stream of satire and libel" that poured forth from this city against Julius. One of the most notorious of such pieces was an open letter from Christ to the pope which has an obvious affinity with the theme of the *Julius* dialogue.[95]

Erasmus may also have seen or heard of similar attacks upon Julius from Germany, especially from the German humanists who opposed him bitterly.[96] But the focal point of European opposition to Julius was Paris. Louis XII had taken up the quixotic Italian adventure of his predecessor and, as a result, it had become the central motive of papal policy to "expell the foreigner" from Italy. The counter-policy of Louis involved not only military campaigns and diplomatic machinations but also a full scale assault upon Julius' spiritual claims. In this enterprise he found support in the traditional Gallicanism of the French clergy, and the king, encouraged by his ambitious minister Cardinal d'Ambroise, put himself at the head of his "national" church, half-leading, half-dragging the French clergy into his fight with the pope. Louis skillfully appealed not only to the Gallican sentiment but to the conciliar precedents of the previous century in the making of which the French clergy and the University of Paris had been instrumental.[97] The so-called Council of Pisa which proved so vexatious to Julius—Erasmus makes him call it a "devil's convention"[98]—was French-inspired and French-dominated and actually grew out of a synod of the Gallican church. The University of Paris found itself once more involved in the conflict with the papacy under the pressure of the court, with learned opinions and counter-opinions hurled back and forth.[99] The court itself became a clearing house for every sort of propaganda against the pope, mounting in volume and heat through the years 1511 and 1512.[100] Louis encouraged every sort of pamphlet, diatribe, satire, and even cartoons showing—for example—the pope standing in armor and surrounded by corpses, or the church complaining that it was sustained only by the strong hand of the French king.[101] The court circle was crowded with silly and pompous "rhetoriqueurs" outdoing one another in the extravagance of their arguments. Even Jean Lemaire de Belges, the royal "historiographer" and the best of this group, wrote a windy and widely circulated tract, *On the Difference between Schisms and Councils of the Church and the Pre-eminence and Utility of Councils of the Holy Gallican Church.* Despite its tediousness, its mediocre logic, and its distortion of facts, it was an effective piece of special pleading, arguing that princes had generally been the advocates of legitimate reform while the popes, by their resistance to councils, had fostered schism—none more so than Julius II.[102]

Louis XII was fond of the theatre and especially of the French form of the *sotie,* a stylized remnant of the medieval morality play, a sort of "Masque of Fools." The *sotie* had already developed into a vehicle of political satire, and Louis enlisted his dramatists in his crusade against Julius.[103] In 1510 or 1511, Pierre Gringore, a special favorite of the king, published his *Hope of Peace,* an eloquent condemnation of papal secularity, in which the poet contrasts Julius with the bishops and martyrs of the early church and contends that the "hope of peace" lies only outside the papacy, in a French-dominated council.[104] At about the same time and on the same theme, Gringore wrote a piece called *The Hunt for the Stag of Stags,* playing on the ancient papal formula, *Servus Servorum Dei, "The Servant of the Servants of God."*[105] But, for our purposes, his most interesting work was *The Jest of the Prince of Fools,* presented publicly in Paris on February 25, 1512, with the king's blessing. Its characters were the French People, the Italian People, Divine Punishment, Simony, Hypocrisy, Mother Fool (the Roman Church), and one called "l'homme obstiné" representing Julius II, wearing the papal tiara and armor, and playing a blustering bully.[106] This is the play to which both Erasmus and More alluded as a possible source of the *Julius exclusus.*[107]

But the play and indeed all the anti-papal propaganda of the French court can be tied in with the *Julius* much more closely than Erasmus and his defenders were willing to admit. Erasmus had spent many years in Paris and had friends in both court and literary circles. Moreover, even failing direct communication, news from France did reach him in England. He might very well have seized upon some of the extravagant charges made against Julius by the French propagandists, for they fell in well with his own feelings toward the pope. Finally, Erasmus probably had an opportunity to see or hear some of these French writings at first hand. He was in Paris briefly in the spring of 1511 to see to the printing of *The Praise of Folly*. At this very time the campaign of Louis XII against the pope was mounting. It was certainly in the forefront of the day-to-day news of the French capital and must have been the prime topic of conversation in the salons, the taverns, the printshops, and publishing houses where Erasmus went.[108]

In the final analysis, however, provocative as such external suggestions may have been, Erasmus really needed no one to tell him that Julius II was brutal, warlike, and a disgrace to the chair of St. Peter; that the cause of reform had been betrayed by the papacy; or that councils were superior to the pope. Moreover, he needed no one to instruct him in literary form. He had played with the satiric dialogue and found it congenial to his temper. As early as the 1490's in Paris he had prepared the first small collection of the *Colloquies*—conversations or dialogues.[109] In England in the fall and winter of 1505 he and Thomas More amused themselves by competing in the translation of some dialogues of Lucian from Greek into Latin. Erasmus' fondness for both the form and content of the Lucianic dialogue continued. He translated some more of them in the fall of 1506 in refuge at Florence from Julius II's attack on Bologna and at least one more during the early months at Cambridge.[110] He was thus thoroughly familiar with the work and style of one of the greatest of ancient satirists. Indeed Erasmus has been called the supreme Lucianist of the Renaissance.

Also, during these years in London and Cambridge, along with his other work, he was preparing the revision of the *Adagia* that Froben would print in 1515. It was this edition in which would appear the long essays "Spartam nactus es, hanc orna," "Sileni Alcibiadis," "Scarabeus aquilam quaerit," and "Dulce bellum inexpertis," filled with his hatred of war, of political manipulation, and of the cynicism of contemporary politics. These were most certainly the raw material for satire. They contain in fact literally dozens of echoes of the *Julius* in theme, references, and usage.[111] This massive revision of the *Adagia* sent Erasmus back once more through the familiar pages of the ancients and doubtless sharpened his already acute sensitivity not only to the substance but to the forms of the classical writers and certainly to the Socratic dialogues, the Greek comedies, and the writings of Horace, Persius, Juvenal, Martial, and Lucian, the classical fathers of satire.[112]

Finally, not two years before the *Julius* was written, as we have seen, Erasmus published the *Praise of Folly,* his greatest work of satire, so close to the *Julius* in some of its themes and spirit, and contained within the stylized classical form of the declamation. He had long since prepared himself to write the *Julius exclusus.* It is easy to imagine that when the news of Julius' death reached him the occasion dictated its own "occasional piece."

The *Julius exclusus* is second only to the *Praise of Folly* among the satiric writings of Erasmus and most closely related to it. It is with the *Praise of Folly* that the *Julius* must inevitably and properly be compared. Both works were born in anger, like most great satire. They share many of the same tricks of speech, rhetoric, and staging. They even attack some of the same abuses. But it is more important to note how they differ, for the essence of the *Julius exclusus* lies there. The *Praise of Folly* is a subtle, highly polished and finished work with its satiric barbs so carefully sheathed in rhetorical devices as to be discovered by the delighted (or infuriated) reader only after they have pricked his hide. The *Julius exclusus* is, in contrast, a sort of static "playlet," truncated and incomplete and impossible to "resolve" in a formal artistic sense. It is true that Julius clumps off stage at the end, muttering and fuming and shaking his stick. But there is no neat resolution of conflict. For this would weaken the author's principal point, and in the *Julius* Erasmus is more advocate than artist. This very point marks the principal difference between the *Praise of Folly* and the *Julius exclusus.*

The *Praise of Folly* is the preeminent example of that revived Greek spirit of irony among the writings of Erasmus, that quality "so subtle and acute" as to belong to him alone in his age. The *Julius exclusus* has much of this spirit of irony and some superb ironic passages. Indeed, the whole work is an extended play on one simple and outrageous ironic situation—that a pope should be denied admittance to heaven! Nothing is spared to maintain it, to emphasize the contrast between the saint, the humble fisherman blessed of Christ and the Holy Spirit and a functionary *inside* heaven, and the lordly pope, blessed only of himself and his sycophants, a functionary of the world and *outside* heaven. Everything else flows from this contrast. The result is not the irony of the *Praise of Folly.* It is rather the most direct, pointed, and malicious kind of invective satire. The *Praise of Folly* was a generalized attack upon folly and human absurdity at which few could take personal offence. But the *Julius* was an explicit attack upon an individual. There is in the *Praise of Folly* that quality of careful contrivance that Kaiser calls "a puzzle of Chinese boxes."[113] We may assume that Erasmus wanted his reader to be somewhat bewildered by Folly's kaleidoscopic rhetoric, tumbling categories, and jumble of opposites. "Whether those opposites are jest and earnest, praise and censure, or wisdom and folly, it is the coincidentia—the synthesis, the equipoise, the concord—which produces the quality of irony."[114] In the *Julius* he wanted no ambiguity. He wanted no one to mistake his point. The irony of the *Praise of Folly* carries with it "a sympathy for human frailty."[115] But the *Julius* never turns to sympathy.

The irony of the *Praise of Folly* and the invective of the *Julius exclusus,* of course, dictate their language. As we have seen, from the earliest comments upon the *Julius* to the present, critics have observed its Erasmian flavor. And it takes no great perception to lay words and phrases and passages from the *Praise of Folly* beside their striking parallels in the *Julius*. Both works contain to an extent the "cruel and dirty words," the "trivial and comic words," and the "colloquial anti-literary words" that Gilbert Highet sees as common to all satire.[116] But the vocabulary of the *Julius* is more cruel, dirty, and colloquial by far than the vocabulary of *Folly*. It is a vocabulary appropriate to invective satire.

Vocabulary, like everything else in the *Julius exclusus,* is subordinate to the purpose that informs the work. For Erasmus was not only an advocate pleading the case against a wicked pope, he was an advocate of reform—not the reform that the religious revolutionaries of his time were about to introduce into the world —but reform nonetheless. Thus the *Julius* is not only an important literary piece, it is also an important document in the moral and intellectual biography of Erasmus.

First of all, it must be related to the work and the ideas of Erasmus as a Christian humanist. He rejected much of the logical methodology, the stylistic framework, and the graceless pedantry of the scholastics, the despised "Thomists and Scotists"—he satirized them dozens of times—in favor of the humanist historicism: back to the sources, whether classical or biblical! Thus the frame of reference of the *Julius* is temporal. Its entire theme, its whole point and impact, derive from a contrast through time; a contrast between Julius II, presented in all his temporality and "with all his imperfections on his head," and the historic, traditional, apostolic character of St. Peter; a contrast between Julius the contemporary vicar of Christ and the scriptural image of Christ himself; and a contrast between the imperfect reality of the present church and the glowing ideal of primitive Christianity. These were certainly not new ideas with Erasmus: they were current in the intellectual milieu of Europe on the eve of the Reformation. In time they became part of the Reformation "theory" in the hands of such men as Luther and Calvin. But Erasmus had no such theory. He was no more a theorist and system-maker than he was a revolutionary. In the course of the *Julius* he argues against the notion of the papacy as an absolute monarchy and for a notion of the community of believers. He asserts the necessity of the imitation of Christ for the pope as for any Christian man. He attacks the wealth and secularism of the church. Needless to say, these were some of the same arguments the revolutionary reformers were shortly to express. But while these arguments were to lead some in the direction of rebellion, Erasmus refused to take that road. He had no real quarrel with the theoretical structure nor the mission of the church, neither in the *Julius* nor elsewhere.

The *Julius* is important also in the list of Erasmus' anti-war writings. It belong with the *Dulce bellum inexpertis* and the *Querela pacis* and expresses the condemnation of war which we find running through all his works like a minor theme. But in the *Julius* this theme has an urgency and specificity which we do not find in his other works. Of all the sins of Julius his war-mongering was, for Erasmus, the most unforgivable. In fact, it is made the main charge of the dialogue.

Closely related to Erasmus' hatred of war, expressed in the *Julius,* is his concern with politics. No one can read the dialogue without being impressed by its wealth of contemporary political detail. Although Erasmus is often wrong in his evaluation of political events, he is deeply concerned with them. If for no other reason, this point is important because it tends to correct a time-honored misconception—that Erasmus was an un-political man. This the author of the *Julius exclusus* most certainly was not.

J. KELLEY SOWARDS

Wichita, Kansas

Translator's Preface

An excellent Latin text of the *Julius exclusus* appears in *Erasmi Opuscula,* edited by Wallace K. Ferguson (The Hague: Martinus Nijhoff, 1933), pp. 38-124. The present translation is based entirely on this text.

The *Julius exclusus* has never been translated into English in its entirety. A number of partial translations exist. The earliest is *The dialoge betwene Julius the seconde, Genius, and saynt Peter* (c. 1533-35), now in the collection of the British Museum (see A. F. Allison and H. M. Nixon, "Three Sixteenth Century English Translations of Erasmus in a Contemporary Binding," *British Museum Quarterly* XXIII (1961), 59-61). The colophon carries the imprint, "At London, by Robert Coplāde, for Johan Byddell, next to flete brydge." There is no date, but Byddell is known to have been at this location from 1533 to 1535. Later, Byddell himself printed an edition of this translation, recording in the colophon his new address at the Sun in Fleet Street, and the date 1535. In these editions, both the author and the translator remain anonymous. The translation deletes every passage which was derogatory of the English and every allusion to Henry VIII. The result is a mutilated work.

Two later English translations belong to the seventeenth and eighteenth centuries:

The Pope Shut out of Heaven Gates: or, A Dialogue between Pope Julius the 2d., His Genius, and Saint Peter . . . Exactly from the Original of the Famous and Learned Erasmus Roterodamus . . . London, Printed for Roger Vaughan in Bishop's Court in the Old-Baily, & are to be sold by the Book-sellers. 1673.

Pope Julius the Second. A Comical and Facetious Dialogue Between Julius II, Evil Genius, and St. Peter. Written originally in *Latin* by The Great Erasmus; And now Translated into *English,* by Philanglus Miso Papas. Lector Risum Cohibe. Dublin: Printed for F. Leathly, at the Corner of Sycamore-Ally, in Dame-street, 1719.

Both translations suffer from the same defects; they rearrange the order of the text and delete substantial passages, and they contain long interpolations distinctly non-Erasmian and much in the manner of late seventeenth century Protestant polemic.

J. A. Froude in his *Life and Letters of Erasmus* (New York, 1912), added, as an appendix to his Lecture VIII (pp. 149-68), "Julius II Exclusus. A dialogue Brought on the Stage at Paris, 1514." The translation is lively and much in the spirit of the original, but it is fragmentary.

The earliest German translation appeared soon after the original publication of the work:

Von dē gewalt vnd haupt der kirchen, ein gesprech, zwischen dem heyligen S. Peter vnd dem allesheyligsten Bapst Jilio . . . dem andern, vnd seyns Genij . . . [1520?].

Two later German translations are based closely upon this earlier version:

Gespräch zwischen St. Peter, Julius II und seinem Schutzgeist an der Himmelspforte gehalten, im Jahre 1513. . . . Frankfort, 1784.

Julius II. Ein Gespräch vor der Himmelsthür. Aus dem Lateinischen des Girolamo Balbi. . . . Berlin, 1877.

The earliest French translation is:

La Vie du Pape Iules Second, Grand Ennemy du Bon Roy Louys Doviesme Roy de France, & des Francois gens de bien tant Ecclesiastiques qu'autres M.D.C.X.V.

Another is included in a collection of *Actes du Concile de Pise,* printed in Paris in 1612, and published separately there in 1727 as *Dialogue entre St. Pierre et Jules II à la porte du Paradis.* Neither French translation identifies the author. There is a later French translation, based on the 1615 version:

Julius, Dialogue entre Saint Pierre et le Pape Jules II à la Porte du Paradis (1513), Attribué à Erasme, à Fausto Andrelini et plus communement à Ulrich de Hutten, traduction nouvelle en regard du Texte Latin par Edmond Thion. Paris, 1875.

There exist also a translation into Danish, and a fairly recent one into Dutch:

Pave Julius Død, en Satire, tr. Fr. Moth, No. 16 of *Studier fra Sprog- og Oldtidsforskning udgivne af det philologisk-historiske Samfund.* Copenhagen, 1894.

Dr. N. Van der Laan, "Erasmus' Satire: Iulius exclusus e Coelis," in *Christendom en Historie.* Zutphen, 1937.

* * *

For the translator, the most noteworthy feature of *Julius exclusus,* and its greatest challenge, is its exceedingly colloquial, almost racy, style and vocabulary. It could have been written only by one who, like Erasmus, was thoroughly familiar with Plautus and Terence. Julius and Genius speak in this style almost exclusively; but even Peter, from his opening words, *Bene habet . . .* (14*), to his closing line, *. . . tam spurcae cloacae defert honorem*

---

* The line numbering in this translation of *Julius exclusus* corresponds as closely as is practical to that of Ferguson's edition. Because of the differences between English and Latin word order, and the greater number of words generally required to express an idea in English than in Latin, the numbering may sometimes be off by a line or two, but rarely, if ever, more than that.

(1225), keeps pace with them in this respect, although his more solemn speeches, especially toward the end of the work, are in appropriately dignified language.

The colloquial quality of the work is seen in single words such as *deglubi* (928), *valde* (1018); diminutives like *muliercula* (164), *leviculis* (530), *pecuniola* (770), *animula* (1063); and many others. I have ventured, with some misgivings, to use such translations as "booze" for *temetum* (72, 83); "gimmick" for *techna,* a favorite Greek word of Plautus (561; also 831, where Peter ironically picks up the word from Julius' earlier use); "damned thunderbolt" for *malum fulmen* (110); and "You slay me" for *obtundis* (990).

Julius has a habit of using *sexcenti* for any moderately large indefinite number, a usage very common in colloquial Latin. I have translated it simply "hundreds" (477, 483, 647, 904, 952). I have also so translated the number *trecenti* (700); the nuance represented by the difference is impossible to reflect without awkwardness in English. Similarly, I translate *sexaginta milia* as "scores of thousands" (1212).

The greatest liberty I have taken in the translation is perhaps not the most conspicuous; that is, the way I have treated the vague connecting words that introduce many sentences in collo-quial English and almost every sentence in colloquial Latin, constituting one of the principal features of that language. In Latin these are such words as *autem, tamen, at, iam, vero, immo, quin, sane, adeo, quidem,* and many more, all of which occur constantly throughout *Julius exclusus.* In colloquial English these may be represented by such words and phrases as "you know," "then," "yes, but," "well," "tell me," "I see," "now," "in fact," and the like. I have freely chosen the English equivalent that seems to me most appropriate to the context regardless of the particular Latin word used in any case; the correspondence be-tween these English and Latin words is tenuous at best, and any attempt at consistency in translating them is likely to be damaging to English idiom, resulting in that strange variety of English often called "translationese." For one example, the slavish translation of the very common Latin particles *nam* and *enim* as "for" produces something alien to English practice, as this is a logical connective that English speakers tend to leave unexpressed except in the most formal discourse; consequently these Latin particles are generally best left untranslated altogether.

Another colloquial element of *Julius exclusus* is the frequent occurrence of cliches and proverbs. These are used mostly by Julius, and they serve to provide a skillful bit of characterization (see for example 210, 726, 859). Even Peter uses one proverbial expression (704), in this case a very learned and obscure one. Erasmus, the compiler of the *Adagia,* was probably more conversant with this sort of material than any other writer of his age. At the time the *Julius exclusus* was written, he was engaged in preparing a new edition of the *Adagia,* to be published by Froben in 1515. Perhaps this may be regarded as adding some support to the argument for Erasmian authorship of the *Julius exclusus.*

In general I subscribe to the principle that a Latin word should, wherever possible, be translated by the same English word every time it occurs. However, particularly in a text of this kind, other considerations frequently render this undesirable. For example, such words as *ingenium* and *invidia,* both very common in *Julius exclusus,* derive a great deal of their force from their context, and particular instances of these words may call for widely varying translations. The exclamation *bona verba!* I have translated once "Talk sense!" (337), once "Don't talk like that!" (952), and twice "Don't use such language!" (475, 788). *Legio* I have translated "regiment" where it refers in a colorless way to an actual military unit of Julius' time (385, 1063), but "legion" in an impassioned speech of Peter (1094). I have translated *superstitiosus* twice as "superstitious" (777, 839); it is amusingly obvious in both of these cases that Julius here means "devout." But once I have felt obliged to translate the same Latin word as "religious" (892), since, while Julius' intention remains the same, the passage would be easily subject to misinterpretation in English if it were translated "superstitious" as before. A clearer example is the play on the words *sanctus* and *sanctitas* (48-66). The Latin adjective means "saintly," and also serves as the specific title for a saint. It is impossible to preserve the play on words here involving the Pope's title *Sua Sanctitas,* because the familiar equivalent in English is "His Holiness," and English speakers naturally do not associate this with "Saint" or "saintly." This, then, is a little joke that must be sacrificed in translation.

Another such joke reluctantly sacrificed is in the use of the word *impensius* (827). I have translated it "more zealously." It also means "at greater expense." It is unfortunate that a translator must commit himself as to whether he thinks avarice or conceit was uppermost in Julius' mind at this point.

Some other nuances I have made an attempt to express in English, hoping for only partial success at best. A rather feeble pun by Julius on the name of the Emperor Maximilian (548) may be preserved by cumbersome means in English. A somewhat better pun by Genius on the literal meaning of *bulla,* "bubble" (53), seems worth going to some effort to preserve. There are many interesting sound effects in the Latin; most of them would result in awkwardness if the attempt were made to convey their force in English. I have succumbed to the temptation to do so only once, in preserving the alliteration in Peter's *nec ullo pacto possit publicam pestem depellere* (464); this is an angry line which Peter may be pictured as literally spitting out. Once, Julius appears to break into a few words of Italian (91); the best solution for a translator here seems to be to leave the phrase in Italian. A particularly interesting point is the way in which Julius refers to himself sometimes as "I," sometimes as "we," evidently depending on whether he is referring to himself in his secular capacity ("I") or as the Vicar of Christ ("we"), but without perfect consistency. I have attempted to translate accordingly. In this regard, see, for example, the repeated shifting between singular and plural at the beginning of Julius' long speech (866 ff.). An interesting corollary to note is that Peter in addressing Julius consistently uses the nonhonorific second person singular. This is a point necessarily obscured in English, where singular and plural coincide in the second person.

I have not translated the important word *Genius,* at the risk of having it associated with its more common meaning as an English word. That Julius should have a Genius, a concept associated with Roman paganism, is an amusing and telling element of the satire; and to give the word its usual translation, "Spirit," would introduce a bit of Christian terminology which would destroy the joke in this context.

Julius' classical allusions are noteworthy (a few examples: 177, 359, 1058). His striking phrase to characterize the decline in the power of the Emperor, *magni nominis umbra* (1041), is actually a quotation from Lucan (I.135); and he begins his account of the reforms proposed by the Gallican council with the words Aeneas uses (Vergil, *Aeneid* 2.204) in beginning the story of Laocoon: *Horresco Referens* (639). Julius uses the exclamation *Hercule!* (726), and is pleased to be referred to as Jupiter (1197). But the most bizarre case of incongruous classical allusion is Julius' attempt to justify his career by quoting to Peter from Aristotle's *Politics* (1163 ff.). Peter himself refers to the classical Lerna in a simile (482; but cf. variant reading *lacunam*); and he refers once to Tartarus (74; cf. Genius, 135); here, to be sure, Peter can point to a truly splendid precedent (Ep. II Peter 2.4).

I have followed Ferguson's text virtually without deviation, despite a number of tempting variants in his apparatus. The few cases where I differ are as follows. In line 42, the text as given yields the opposite of the sense evidently required. I emend *didicisti* to *dedidicisti*. Another possible emendation would be *si* for *nisi,* yielding the sense, ". . . that is, if you have learned the alphabet altogether"; but the first seems an easier error to account for. In line 297, I translate *nomine* for the unintelligible *nomen* (note variant reading *numine* in apparatus). In line 986, I translate *et* for *te;* this is presumably a mere typographical error in the edition. In line 1131, the variant reading *alienissimum* seems preferable to the *alienissimam* that Ferguson prints, and *simillimam* of line 1130 should accordingly be emended to *simillimum;* I have so translated. I suspect that Ferguson has misinterpreted this sentence altogether, as he erroneously places a comma after *sui* (1130), instead of after *Ecclesiam* where it belongs. There are, in fact, many errors of punctuation in Ferguson's edition, some of which are serious enough to interfere with comprehension of the passages in which they occur. The remark of Genius in line 57 is an interruption of Julius' speech, so there should be no full stop indicated at 56; the same observation applies also to 1137 (unless the unlikely variant *an* for *ni* in line 1139 be accepted). In line 513 there should be a comma after *propalam.* In line 561, the comma after *suppliciter* should be deleted; Ferguson seems to regard this adverb as one of the series of verbs. In line 1046, no new sentence begins after *sequereris.*

I have tried to avoid the temptation to add interpretative material to my translation, but in a few cases it seemed preferable to do so rather than to leave a point obscure. In line 118, my translation, ". . . and nothing more than any other lay priest," represents the puzzling Latin *nec aliud quam quilibet privatus sacerdos* rather loosely. It may be that the variant *plebeius* for *privatus* is to be preferred here altogether. In line 123, my translation,

". . . you are no more superior to me than any dead man," for *nihilo mihi praestas plus quam mortuus,* awkward as it is, is an attempt to compensate for the excessive condensation of the Latin. In line 189, where I translate "any other office" there is nothing in the Latin that represents the words "any other"; I hope this is an excusable liberty, as its only motive is clarity.

I must conclude by observing that I continue to find several passages obscure. These include line 239: *Hoc tametsi durum videtur, molle quiddam est* (I suspect an obscene reference); line 797: *si cetera conveniant;* and line 1085: *immo et quod non poteras.* If this last is the correct reading, Ferguson's question mark should be deleted; the passage would be easier if the variant reading *quid* for *et quod* were accepted, in which case it would in fact be a question, and the sense would be, "But what power did you lack?"

PAUL PASCAL

Seattle, Washington

THE *JULIUS EXCLUSUS* OF ERASMUS

Julius Excluded from Heaven

A Dialogue

Cast: JULIUS,
GENIUS,
PETER

JULIUS: What the devil is going on here? Doors won't open, eh? Looks as if the lock has been changed, or tampered with, anyway.

GENIUS: You'd better check and see that you didn't bring the wrong key. You don't open this door, you know, with the same one that opens your money-box. In fact, why didn't you bring them both? The one you have there is the key to power, not to knowledge.

JULIUS: Well, this is the only one I ever had; and I don't see why I need that other one when I have this one.[1]

GENIUS: I don't either, to be sure—except that meanwhile we *are* locked out.

10 JULIUS: I'm getting fed up. I'll pound on the door. Hey, come on! Open this door right away, somebody! What's going on? No one here. Why is that gatekeeper taking so long? I suppose he's snoring, good and drunk.

45

GENIUS: How this man measures everyone by himself!

PETER: Well, it's a good thing we have a gate like iron. Otherwise this fellow, whoever he is, would have broken the doors down. It must be that some giant or satrap, a sacker of cities, has arrived. But, immortal God, what a sewer I smell here! I won't open the door right away, but I'll look out of the barred window here and find out what this portent may be. Who are you? And what do you want?

20 JULIUS: How about opening the door, you, right away! If you wanted to do your job right you would have come to meet me —with the whole parade of angels, in fact.

PETER: Pretty bossy, all right. But first, you tell me who you are.

JULIUS: As if you don't see for yourself!

PETER: See? As far as I'm concerned, I see a strange spectacle, one I have never seen before—not to say a monstrosity.

JULIUS: But unless you're just plain blind, I trust you recognize this key, in case you don't know the golden oak.[2] And you do see the triple crown, as well as this robe shining all over with jewels and gold.[3]

30 PETER: I recognize the silver key, more or less; although there is just the one,[4] and that quite unlike the ones that the true shepherd of the Church, Christ, once entrusted to me. But that arrogant crown you have, how, pray, would I be able to recognize that? Not even a barbarian tyrant has ever ventured to flaunt such a thing as that, still less anyone who expects to be admitted here. As for the robe, that impresses me not at all, since I have always trampled upon and despised jewels and gold as if they were rubbish. But what is this? Wherever I look, on the key, on the crown, and on the robe, I see the mark of that most wicked huckster and impostor, who has my first name, to be sure, but not my calling—Simon, whom I once cast down by the aid of Christ.[5]

40 JULIUS: Cut out the foolishness, if you have any sense. For your

46

information, I am the famous Julius the Ligurian,[6] and I trust you recognize the letters P.M., unless you've forgotten the alphabet altogether.

PETER: I take it they stand for Pestilential Maximum.

GENIUS: Ho, ho! How this soothsayer has hit the nail on the head!

JULIUS: Oh, come on—they stand for Pontifex Maximus, the supreme Pontiff.

PETER: You may be thrice *maximus,* and even more so than the famous Mercury Trismegistus, but you will not be received here unless you have been *optimus,* that is saintly.[7]

JULIUS: As far as that goes, if it does mean anything to be called "saintly," you're exceedingly impudent to delay in opening the doors for me, when for so many centuries now you have only been called "saint," while no one has ever called me anything but "most saintly." There exist thousands of Bulls—

GENIUS: Really bu-bbles!

JULIUS: —in which I am called again and again "most holy lord"; in fact, I used to be designated not as "holy," but by the very name of "holiness";[8] so that whatever I took a notion to do—

GENIUS: Even when he was drunk![9]

JULIUS: —they would say that "the holiness of the most holy lord Julius" had done it.

PETER: Well, then, demand heaven of those same flatterers who have made you "most holy"; and let the same men reward you with bliss, who have given you holiness. But do you honestly believe there is no difference between being called holy and *being* holy?

JULIUS: This is really exasperating! If only I had been allowed to remain alive, I wouldn't envy you now either for that holiness of yours, or for your bliss.

PETER: Oh, what a holy mind that utterance reveals![10] Still, even aside from that, for a long time now I've been scrutinizing you, and I observe many a mark of godlessness, but not one of holiness. For example, what is the meaning of that strange, unpontifical retinue of yours? You have tens of thousands of men with you, and I do not perceive in so great a mob any one who so much as *looks* like a Christian. What I do see is a most foul conglomeration of men that smell of nothing but brothels, booze, and gunpowder. It looks to me as if mercenary brigands, or even specters from Tartarus, have swarmed here from the underworld, to make war on heaven.[11] And as for yourself, the more I contemplate you, the less do I see any trace of an apostolic man. To begin with, what monstrosity is this: while you wear on the outside the splendid attire of a priest, at the same time underneath you are altogether horrendous with the clatter of bloody weapons? And then how fierce are your eyes, how nasty your mouth, how baleful your expression, how haughty and arrogant your brow![12] I am ashamed to say, and at the same time disgusted to observe, that there is no part of your body that is not befouled by the marks of portentous and execrable lust; to say nothing of the fact that even now you are all belches and the smell of drunkenness and booze; and in fact you appear to me to have just finished vomiting. In any event, such is the bearing of your whole body that you appear shriveled, rotted, and broken, not so much by age and disease as by drunkenness.

GENIUS: How graphically his rhetoric has depicted this man!

PETER: Though for some time I've observed you giving me threatening looks, nevertheless I cannot suppress what I feel. I suspect that most pestilential pagan Julius has returned in disguise from the underworld to mock me; so completely is everything in you consistent with him.[13]

JULIUS: *Ma di si!*

PETER: What did he say?

GENIUS: He's angry. At those words, there isn't one of the Cardinals who didn't beat a retreat, since he would otherwise soon feel the cudgel of the most holy one—especially after a carouse.[14]

PETER: Now *you* seem to me to be quite clever in interpreting the man; so, tell me, who are you?

GENIUS: I am the mighty Genius of Julius.

PETER: Rather the evil Genius, I imagine.

GENIUS: Whatever I am, I am of Julius.

JULIUS: Why don't you cut out the nonsense and open the door, unless you would rather have it battered down? In a word—do you see what a retinue I have?

PETER: To be sure, I see thoroughly hardened brigands. But, in case you don't know it, these doors you must storm with other weapons.

JULIUS: Enough talk, I say! Unless you obey right away, I shall hurl—even against *you*—the thunderbolt of excommunication, with which I once terrified the mightiest of kings, or for that matter whole kingdoms. You see the Bull already prepared for this purpose?

PETER: What damned thunderbolt, what thunder, what Bulls, what bombast are you talking to me about, pray? We never heard anything about those matters from Christ.

JULIUS: Well, you'll feel them, if you don't obey.

PETER: Maybe you terrified some people with that hot air before, but it means nothing here. Here you have to operate with the truth. This citadel is won by good deeds, not by evil words. But, I beg of you, do *you* threaten *me* with the thunderbolt of excommunication? Tell me, by what right?

JULIUS: A perfectly good right, since you're a layman now, and nothing more than any other lay priest; not even a priest at that, since you have no power to consecrate.[15]

PETER: You mean because I'm dead, I suppose.

49

JULIUS: That's the general idea.

PETER: But by that reasoning you are no more superior to me than any dead man.

JULIUS: Not so. As long as the Cardinals bicker about electing a new Pope, it's my administration.[16]

GENIUS: How he still dreams the dreams of the living!

JULIUS: Now come on and open up, I say!

PETER: And *I* say, if you do not give me a recital of your merits, you won't accomplish a thing.

130 JULIUS: What do you mean, merits?

PETER: I'll tell you. Did you excel in theology?

JULIUS: Certainly not. There was no time, for a man who was busy with so many wars. But there are plenty of friars, if that helps any.

PETER: Well then, did you win many for Christ by the holiness of your life?

GENIUS: For Tartarus, a great many.

PETER: Were you famous for miracles?

JULIUS: They're out of style!

PETER: Did you pray with a pure heart, and constantly?

JULIUS: How he does run on!

140 PETER: Furthermore, did you mortify your flesh with fasts and vigils?

GENIUS: Oh, cut it out. This isn't getting you anywhere. Don't waste the effort on this man.

PETER: I know of no other gifts of a proper Pope. If he has any that are more apostolic, let him tell of them himself.

JULIUS: Though it is degrading for the famous Julius, hitherto invincible, to submit now to Peter, who is, to say the least, a fisherman and practically a beggar; nevertheless, so you'll know what sort of a prince you're insulting, listen a bit. To begin with, I am a Ligurian, not a Jew like you; and I regret having

150 even this much in common with you, that I was once a boatman.

GENIUS: Don't let it bother you; there is a big difference here too, in that he used to fish to get food, but you pulled an oar for a pittance.[17]

JULIUS: Furthermore, Sixtus, a Pontiff really supreme—

GENIUS: In vices, he means.

JULIUS: —was my maternal uncle.[18] Through his special favor and my own industry, I was raised, first to ecclesiastical wealth, and then step by step to the eminence of a Cardinal's hat;[19] then I was tested by many storms of fortune and hurled up and down by terrible mischances. I was subject to the falling sickness[20] as well as other ailments; finally I was covered all over with the so-called French pox.[21] Added to all this I was an exile, hated, damned, degraded before all, and practically given up for lost.[22] Nevertheless, I myself never let go of my hope for the supreme Pontificate. Such was the strength of my spirit; while you, when terrified by the voice of a mere woman, gave up immediately.[23] As for you, a woman took your courage away; as for me, a woman, a soothsayer or fortune teller, gave me the confidence I have by secretly whispering into my ear once when I was sunk in many troubles, "Persevere, scion of the Julii! Don't be disgusted by anything you have to do or put up with. One day you will be graced with the triple crown. You will be king of kings and lord of those that rule."[24] And in fact I was not deceived, either by my hope or by her prophecy. And I have fought my way to this position without anyone's expecting it, partly through the aid of the French, who gave me refuge when I was cast out,[25] partly by the vast power of money raised by usury; but also not without real ability.

PETER: What ability do you mean?

JULIUS: I mean, not without priesthoods promised for a consideration, and a careful search for those able to give security for them, since a sum so huge as that even Crassus would hardly have been able to pay in cash and in full. But it's pointless for

51

me to tell you about this, when it's something that not even
all the bankers understand.[26] Now you know how I got there.
Well then, in my Pontificate I carried on in such a way that
there is no one—I don't mean those primitive Popes who seem
to me to have been Popes in name only, I mean even the more
recent ones—to whom the Church, to whom Christ himself,
owes so much, as to me.

GENIUS: How Thrasonical the beast is acting![27]

PETER: I'm waiting to hear what comes next.

JULIUS: By discovering many new so-called offices, I enlarged
the Papal treasury in no small way. Then I invented a system
whereby bishoprics could be bought without the sin of simony.
It had been provided by my predecessors that whoever became
a bishop had to resign any other office. This I interpreted as
follows: "You are bidden to resign; but you cannot resign
what you do not have; so you have to buy something to resign."
By this device, single bishoprics instantly brought in six or
seven thousand ducats each, in addition to the sum customarily
extorted for Bulls.[28] Then from the new currency with which
I glutted all Italy I made no little profit.[29] I neglected nothing
in accumulating money; I knew after all that without this
nothing goes well, either sacred or profane. And to get to
bigger things, when Bologna had been occupied by the Bentivogli, I restored it to the Roman See. The Venetians, previously not conquered by anyone, I crushed in battle. As for
the Duke of Ferrera, after harrying him in war for a long time,
I almost lured him into a trap. I neatly disposed of a schismatic
council by faking a counter-council, and, as the saying goes, I
used a nail to drive a nail.[30] Finally I drove the French, who
were then the terror of the whole world, completely out of
Italy. And I was going to drive out the Spaniards too, as that
was my next project, if the Fates had not snatched me from the
earth. And in this matter too, consider what invincible courage

I displayed. When the French had the upper hand, I began to look about for a place to hide. I was growing a white beard,[31] since the situation had become practically hopeless, when suddenly there comes the golden news that several thousand French had been slaughtered at Ravenna.[32] At that, Julius came back to life. Come to think of it, I was for three days actually considered to be on the point of death, even by myself. And once more I was revived, counter to everyone's expectation, even my own.[33] So great, then, is the power of my authority—or maybe of my cunning—that today there are no Christian kings whom I have not provoked to arms, rending, tearing, and shattering all the treaties by which they had been closely bound together. Most recently even the Treaty of Cambrai, which I entered upon with the King of the French, the King of the Romans, and other princes, has been so obliterated that there is never even any mention of it.[34] Above and beyond all this, even though I supported such a great army, celebrated so many splendid triumphs, held so many festivals, erected buildings in so many places; still, when I died I left five million ducats.[35] And I was planning bigger things, if that Jewish doctor who had prolonged my life by his art for so long had been able to protract it further.[36] And if only some magician would restore me to life again now, so I could set the final seal on my enterprises so nobly begun! Still, when I died, I took great pains to insure that the wars I had stirred up all over the world should not be settled, and I saw to it that the money set aside for just that purpose would remain safe. This was my last utterance as I breathed out my soul.[37] And now do you begrudge opening the doors of heaven for a Pope who has deserved so well of Christ and of the Church? And all this will be even more amazing if you consider that I achieved it by virtue of the strength of my will alone, aided by none of the advantages that others generally have—not by high birth, since I don't even know my father[38] (and I say it proudly); not by beauty, since everyone shuddered at my ghastly face; not by learning, which I never acquired;[39] not by strength of body, since my body was as I have described it to you; not by the favor accorded youth, since I did these things as an old man; not by popular support, since everyone hated me; not by clemency, since I was so inexorable that I was even fierce to those to whom other men are usually very indulgent—

PETER: What does he mean?

GENIUS: Though it sounds like harshness, he really means something quite soft.

240 JULIUS: —but although opposed by fortune, age, physique, in short, by gods and by men, nevertheless, relying solely on my strength of will and on money, I accomplished these great things in a few years, leaving so much raw material for posterity that they will have enough to keep them busy for ten years. This much I have said about myself, in perfect truth but in perfect modesty; if one of those men who makes speeches before me in Rome had embellished this with his rhetorical trappings, you would be hearing a god, not a man.

PETER: Most invincible warrior, since all the things you are telling me about are new and unheard of to me, I beg you to pardon my stupidity or my inexperience and not let it annoy you to have to answer one interrogating you so clumsily on individual points. Who are those fair curly-haired ones?

250 JULIUS: Those I kept for my pleasure.[40]

PETER: And who are those dark ones, covered with scars?

JULIUS: They are the soldiers and commanders who for my sake and for the Church met death bravely in war, some in capturing Bologna, a great number in the battle against the Venetians, many at Ravenna; and to all of them heaven is due by special arrangement, since long ago by mighty Bulls I promised that those men who fought under the auspices of Julius would fly straight to heaven, no matter what kind of life they had led before.[41]

PETER: Now I think I finally understand! Those were the men who often before your arrival pestered me by trying to break in here by all means short of violence, brandishing those ponderous Bulls.

JULIUS: So, you didn't let them in, I gather?

PETER: I? Not a single one of that breed. For this is what Christ instructed me: these doors are to be opened not for those who come bringing Bulls heavy with lead, but for those who have clothed the naked, fed the hungry, given drink to the thirsty, come to those in prison, and welcomed strangers.[42] In fact, if He wanted to exclude even those who prophesied in His name, who cast out devils, who did wonderful works,[43] do you suppose that those men should be admitted who bring no more than a Bull signed by Julius?

JULIUS: If I had found out —!

PETER: I know, if someone had returned from the underworld and informed you of this, you would have declared war on me.

JULIUS: Why, I would have excommunicated you besides.

PETER: Well, let's go on. Why are you in armor yourself?

JULIUS: As if you didn't know that the supreme Pontiff possesses both swords;[44] or else perhaps you would want a man to wage war naked.

PETER: As for me, when I held your position, I knew no sword but the sword of the spirit, which is the word of God.[45]

JULIUS: But that's not borne out by Malchus, whose ear you cut off—without a sword, I suppose![46]

PETER: I remember, and I acknowledge it. But then I was fighting for my master, Christ, not for myself; for the life of the Lord, not for money or secular dominion; and when I fought I was not yet Pope, since the keys had been only promised, not yet received, nor had I yet received the Holy Spirit.[47] But even so I was ordered to put up my sword, so that I might be clearly admonished that this kind of fight was unbecoming to priests, in fact to any Christians.[48] But we'll talk about that some other time. Why do you make such a point of proclaiming yourself a Ligurian? As if it made any difference to the Vicar of Christ what his nationality was.

JULIUS: On the contrary, I consider it the very height of piety to ennoble my nation; consequently I inscribe this title on all my coins, statues, arches, and walls.[49]

PETER: So he knows his fatherland, who does not know his father. And I thought at first that you were speaking of the heavenly Jerusalem, the fatherland of those that believe, and about its single prince, in whose name those men hope to be sanctified, that is illuminated. But why do you add, "A nephew of Sixtus, by his sister"? I wonder at the fact that the man has not arrived here, especially when he was both the supreme Pontiff and a relative of such a mighty general as you. So tell me, pray, what sort of man was he? A priest?

JULIUS: No, he was an outstanding military man, and a member of a distinguished religious order as well, namely the Franciscan.[50]

PETER: Now I did once meet a Francis, the best of men among the laity, one who had supreme contempt for wealth, pleasure, and ambition. Does a poor little fellow like that have such satraps now?

JULIUS: As far as I can see, you would be unwilling for anyone to better his condition. Benedict was a pauper too, and his followers are so rich now that even we envy them.

PETER: Bravo! But to get back to the subject; about your being a nephew of Sixtus.

JULIUS: I say that on purpose, naturally, to shut the mouths of the people who somewhat too freely assert that I am his son.[51]

PETER: Freely, but—actually, is it true?

JULIUS: But that would not be in keeping with the dignity of the Pope, which must be taken into account in all matters.

PETER: But that very dignity, it seems to me, will give the most proper account of itself when it does nothing for which it can rightly be blamed. But I beg of you, by the majesty of the Pope, tell me honestly, is what you just described the common and accepted way now of achieving the supreme Pontificate?

JULIUS: For several centuries now there has been no other way, unless perhaps my successor will be elected by another. I myself, once I achieved the supreme Pontificate, immediately took precautions, through a fearsome Bull, that no one else should reach that honor by the same means. I also renewed that Bull shortly before I died.[52] How effective it will be, others will see.

PETER: I am sure there is no one who could have described that particular evil more accurately. But one thing amazes me: that anyone can be found who is willing to undertake this office, when it is subject, I understand, to so many responsibilities, and when it takes such effort to fight for it. When I was Pope, hardly anyone could be induced even by force to undertake the office of a bishop or a deacon.

JULIUS: No wonder; for in those days the lot and reward of bishops was nothing but hardship, vigils, fasts, study, and often death. Now it is a kingship and a tyranny. And who wouldn't fight for a kingdom, if he had the chance?

PETER: All right, how about Bologna? Had it lapsed from the faith, so that it had to be restored to the Roman See?

JULIUS: Talk sense! That's not what it was about.

PETER: Perhaps Bentivoglio's administration was so bad that the state was languishing?

JULIUS: No, as a matter of fact it was flourishing. It was a city that had been enlarged and embellished by many buildings; and on that account I was all the more avid for it.

PETER: I understand. So, he had occupied it unlawfully?

JULIUS: Not even that; he was holding it by consent.

PETER: So the citizens couldn't stand him as prince?

JULIUS: On the contrary, they clung to him tooth and nail; almost all of them opposed me.[53]

PETER: What reason was there then?

JULIUS: Simply that he conducted his administration in such a way that, from the immense sum he collected from the citizens, only a few thousands found their way to our treasury. Furthermore, it was expedient for the plans that I had in mind at that moment. So, with the French eagerly cooperating, some of them frightened by my thunderbolts, I drove out Bentivoglio and set Cardinals and bishops over the city, so that every bit of its revenues would be at the service of the Church of Rome.[54] Furthermore, before this the name and dignity of empire were visibly attached to him.[55] But now everywhere you look *our* statues are seen, *our* titles are read, *our* trophies are venerated. Now Julius stands everywhere in stone and in bronze. In short, if you had seen with what a royal triumph I entered Bologna, I'll bet you would despise all the triumphs of the Octavii and the Scipios, and you would realize it was with good reason that I fought so hard for Bologna. And you would have seen the Church truly militant and triumphant at the same time.

PETER: So, I suppose, with your reign there has come to pass that for which Christ ordered us to pray: "Thy Kingdom come."[56] But now the Venetians, what had they done?

JULIUS: In the first place they were acting like Greeks, and they were making sport of me, hurling all sorts of slanders at me.

PETER: True ones or false?

JULIUS: What difference does it make? It is sacrilege even to whisper about the Roman Pope, except in his praise. Besides, they were bestowing priesthoods by their own choice. They allowed no trials to be referred to our courts; they purchased no dispensations. Need I say more? They were causing the Roman See an intolerable loss, and furthermore they were usurping no small part of *your* patrimony.[57]

PETER: *My* patrimony? What patrimony, pray, are you talking about to me who, forsaking everything, myself naked, followed the naked Christ?[58]

JULIUS: I mean several towns that are bound to the Roman See. That is what the most holy fathers liked to call their own private part of their possessions.[59]

80 PETER: By slandering me you take good care of your own profits. So, this loss you call intolerable?

JULIUS: Of course—why not?

PETER: But were their ways corrupt? Had their piety flagged?

JULIUS: Oh, come on, don't be silly. The fact is that we were being cheated of countless thousands of ducats, as many in fact as would suffice to maintain a regiment of soldiers.

PETER: A great loss indeed for a loan shark. But the Duke of Ferrara, tell me, what had he done?

JULIUS: That man, the greatest ingrate of all? That famous Vicar of Christ, Alexander, held him in such honor that he 90 gave him his second daughter in marriage, and he added as a dowry a most splendid realm; and this to a man who had no ambition. Nevertheless, oblivious to such kindness, he was always snarling at me, calling me a simoniac, a pederast, and a lunatic. Furthermore, he claimed certain revenues as his own; not very important ones, to be sure, but nevertheless not to be spurned by a careful shepherd.[60]

GENIUS: Tycoon, he means.

JULIUS: Furthermore, what is more to the point, this is something else that was expedient for what I was planning: that this power should be united with my realm, because of its strategic location. So I ventured, when I got rid of him, to 100 bestow that realm on a relative of mine, a vigorous man, and

59

one who would dare anything at all for the dignity of the Church; as witness that he had recently stabbed the Cardinal of Pavia with his own hand, as a favor to me. As for my daughter's husband, he was satisfied with his lot.[61]

PETER: Do you mean to tell me that Popes have wives and children?

JULIUS: Well, they don't have wives of their own, of course. But what's so strange about their having children, since they're men, not eunuchs?

PETER: Now tell me, what was it that provoked that schismatic council?

JULIUS: It would take a very long time to begin right at the beginning; I will give you just the high points. Now there were some people who were beginning to get sick of the Roman Curia. They said that it was all befouled by shameful commerce, unnatural and unspeakable lusts, sorcery, sacrilege, murder, and simoniacal marketplaces on every hand. Even me they called a simoniac, a drunkard, filthy, swollen with worldly spirit, and in every respect unworthily occupying that post, to the utter ruin of Christendom; so they would have to summon a general council to combat these afflictions. Furthermore they said that I had been bound by oath to convoke a general council within two years after I took office, and that I had been elected Pope on that condition.[62]

PETER: And were they telling the truth?

JULIUS: Absolutely. But I personally released myself from that oath when I thought it best.[63] Who would hesitate to swear to anything at all, when it is a question of a kingdom? It is in other matters that piety is to be cultivated, as was elegantly observed by that famous Julius, my alter ego.[64] Now just look how audacious men are; see what they did next. Nine Cardinals defect; they send *me* official notice of a council; they invite me and plead with me to preside. When they don't have their way, they proclaim it to all, by the authority of Maximilian as

410

420

Emperor (claiming that history bears witness that once councils were proclaimed by the Roman Emperors), and likewise
by the authority of Louis XII of France (I shudder to name
him); and they tried to rip apart that coat of Christ's without
seam, which even those who crucified Him left intact.[65]

PETER: But were you the kind of person they kept saying you
were?

JULIUS: What does that matter? I was Pope. Let's say that I was
even more evil than the Cercopes, even stupider than Morychus, or less learned than a block of wood, filthier than Lerna:[66]
whoever holds this key of power, it is proper to revere him as
the Vicar of Christ, to regard him as most holy.

PETER: Even one who is openly evil?

JULIUS: Even as openly as can be. It is intolerable that he who
represents God on earth—in fact is something of an actual
God among men—should be criticized by any mere human
being, or subject to reproaches.

PETER: And yet common sense cries out against our being well
disposed to anyone we observe to be manifestly criminal, or
speaking well of anyone about whom we hear ill.

JULIUS: Let each man think what he pleases, as long as he
speaks favorably, or at least shuts up. In short, the Roman
Pope cannot be criticized, not even by a general council.[67]

PETER: All I know is that the man who sustains the role of
Christ on earth ought to be as much like Him as possible, and
he ought to pass his whole life in such a way that nothing in
him can be criticized, or that no one can justifiably speak ill
of him. There's something wrong with the Popes if they ex-
tort men's good opinion by threats rather than win it by good
works; if you can't praise them except by lying; if their greatest glory is to have compelled the silence of men who think
ill of them. But now tell me truthfully, is there no way that a
criminal and pestilent Pope can be removed?

JULIUS: Don't be silly. Who's to remove the man at the top?

PETER: And yet that is the best reason why he has to be removed,
460   that he is at the top. The greater he is, the more damage he
can do. If the laws of the world not only depose a ruler who
administers the state badly, but actually sentence him to death,
what is the sorry condition of the Church, that it is forced to
put up with a Pope at Rome who subverts everything, and it
has no possibility of disposing of a public pest by any process?

JULIUS: But if the Pope of Rome is to be chastised, he must be
chastised through a council; and no council can be convoked
against the Pope's will, otherwise it would be a mere convention, not a council. And, at best, if it should be convoked, it
could not pass anything if the Pope opposed it. As a last resort
there remains his ultimate bulwark, namely absolute power,
470   by which one Pope is far superior even to a universal council.
Furthermore, he cannot be removed from his priesthood for
any crime whatever.

PETER: Not for murder?

JULIUS: Not even for parricide.

PETER: Not for fornication?

JULIUS: Don't use such language! But in fact, not even for
incest.

PETER: Not even for simoniacal impiety?

JULIUS: Not even for hundreds of instances.

PETER: Not for sorcery?

JULIUS: Not even for sacrilege.

480   PETER: Not for blasphemy?

JULIUS: No, I tell you.

PETER: Not for all these things at once, combined into a single
Lerna, so to speak?

JULIUS: Name, if you like, hundreds of crimes besides, ones
even fouler than these—nevertheless the Pope at Rome cannot
be removed from his office on account of them.

PETER: Well, you make it sound like a new privilege for the

Roman Pope if he alone can be utterly evil with impunity. Still more, a new grief for the Church, if there is no way it can rid itself of such a monster, and if it is obliged to worship a Pope such as no one would have for a stable boy.

JULIUS: There are some who say that he can be removed for just one reason.

PETER: Well, do tell me now, for what good deed? Obviously he can't be removed for an evil deed, if he can't for those I mentioned.

JULIUS: For the crime of heresy.[68] But at that, only if he has been publicly convicted. But even this is a mere bagatelle, and it doesn't interfere the least bit with the Pontifical majesty. In the first place, it's within his power to abrogate the very law, if he doesn't like it. Then, who'd dare to bring charges against the supreme Pontiff, when he is protected by so many weapons? Furthermore, if he should happen to be subject to pressure by a council, it's easy for him to make a recantation, if he can't deny the whole thing. In short, there are a thousand loopholes by which he can easily get away with it—unless, to be sure, he is a blockhead, not a man.

PETER: But, by the power of the Pope, tell me, who made such splendid laws?

JULIUS: Who else but the fount of all laws, the Roman Pope? Furthermore, it's the privilege of that same person to abrogate the law, interpret it, expand it, limit it—whatever seems to suit his own advantage.

PETER: Happy indeed is the Pope if he can pass a law by which he can even make a mockery of Christ, to say nothing of a council. And yet against such a Pope as you just described— manifestly criminal, drunken, a murderer, simoniacal, a sorcerer, a perjurer, grasping, befouled in every part by monstrous varieties of lust, and very conspicuously so—it is not a general council that is to be hoped for so much as that the

63

people, armed with stones, should publicly remove him from their midst as a pest to the world. But now tell me, what is the reason that you, as Pope of Rome, shudder so at the thought of a general council?

JULIUS: Why don't you ask monarchs why they hate a senate and general assemblies? The fact is, when so many outstanding men gather together, the royal dignity is overshadowed to a certain extent; the educated men derive confidence and daring from their learning; the good men, secure in their conscience, speak more freely than is expedient for us; the well-born make good use of their authority. And among these there also appear men who envy our glory, and bring with them the intention of diminishing both the wealth and the authority of the Pope. In short, there is no one at such a session who does not imagine that he has certain rights, by virtue of its being a council, against the Pope, who is clearly invincible on other occasions. As a result, hardly any council has ever turned out so well that the supreme Pontiff has not experienced some loss to his majesty, and departed less supreme. To this even you yourself can bear witness, unless it has slipped your mind altogether; though to be sure in those days very trivial matters were involved, not empires and royal fortunes as now, nevertheless, James ventured to add to your speech something of his own; specifically, when you would have liberated the Gentiles altogether from the burden of the Mosaic law, James spoke after you and excepted fornication, and blood, and sacrifices to idols, as if to correct your opinion;[69] so that even today there are some who are moved by this episode to regard not you, but James, as having the authority of the supreme Pontiff.

PETER: Then do you think that the only thing worth looking out for is that the royal majesty of the supreme Pontiff should be secure, and not rather the general interest of the Christian commonwealth?

JULIUS: Each man looks out for his own interest; we take care of our business.

PETER: And yet, if Christ had done that, that Church would not now even exist, of which you boast that you are the monarch. And I don't see how it makes sense that the man who rejoices at being called the Vicar of Christ has goals different from those of Christ. But now tell me, by what device did you dispose of that schismatic council, as you call it?

JULIUS: Well, I'll tell you and you follow me if you can. In the first place, the Emperor Maximilian (that's his name, all right), is of all men minimally difficult,[70] and although he had proclaimed the council by solemn pronouncements, nevertheless I seduced him from his intention[71] by means better left unsaid. Furthermore, by similar devices I persuaded several Cardinals that they should once more summon notaries and witnesses and deny what they had stated in documents already published.[72]

PETER: Can that be done?

JULIUS: Why can't it be done if the supreme Pontiff approves?

PETER: What? If he wishes it, then, an oath is not an oath, since it is something from which he can absolve anyone he wants.

JULIUS: Well to be perfectly honest, that particular case was a little too blatant, but there was no more convenient way open. Then, when I saw that a number of men were going to hate me as a result of the council, especially since it had been announced in such terms that I was not excluded, but respectfully invited and urged to preside, see what a gimmick I found, following the example of my predecessors. I myself issued a summons to a council, alleging that neither the time nor the place which they had proposed was suitable. I announced the council at Rome immediately, and I thought that no one would come to it who was not friendly to Julius, or at least who would not support him—I had trained them for this by many examples—and for this purpose I instantly created a number of Cardinals amenable to my plans.

GENIUS: That is to say, utter scoundrels.

570 JULIUS: Again, if I had not announced this council, there would not have been a council. And yet it was by no means convenient for my affairs that so great a throng of bishops and abbots should flock here; there were bound to be some upright and pious men among them. So I warned them to save expenses and send only one or two men for each region. Then when I saw that even this would not be safe enough, and that a few men from so many provinces would amount to a great number, finally when they were all packed for the trip, I told them not to come, that the council had to be postponed to another date, making up more or less plausible reasons for this. And when one and all had been turned away by this device, this time
580 *anticipating* the date I had set, I held a council at Rome, with only those whom I had prepared for this purpose. And even though there were likely to be some among them who would disagree with me, nevertheless I regarded it as certain that no one was going to oppose Julius, who was so superior in arms and supporters.[73] Now in this fashion I aroused great hatred against that Gallican council: I sent letters in every possible direction, in which I referred to our sacrosanct council, execrated their council, and called it Satan's get-together, the devil's convention, a schismatic conspiracy.[74]

PETER: The Cardinals who were the authors and leaders of the
590 council must have been very evil men.

JULIUS: About their character I make no complaint. But the head of the whole business was the Cardinal of Rouen,[75] who through a kind of sanctimoniousness was always looking to reform the Church. And in some respects he succeeded. Death took him away, doing me the most grateful of services. His successor was the Cardinal of Santa Croce,[76] a Spaniard, of blameless life to be sure, but an inflexible old man and a theologian—this is a type of man that causes the Popes at Rome a lot of trouble.

PETER: And did a man who was a theologian find no plausible way to justify his action?

JULIUS: Oh, a great many. He said there had never been times less quiet than those, and that the Church had never been afflicted with more unbearable ailments; so there had to be recourse to a general council. He said that when I had been admitted to the supreme Pontificate, I had been bound by sacred oaths that in the second year after my entrance into the Pontificate I should proclaim a council—bound, in fact, in such a way that I could not be absolved even by a conclave of the Cardinals; and then that, although frequently advised and asked by my brother Cardinals and importuned by princes, I had lent my ears to any matter at all rather than to this; so that it was quite obvious that while Julius was alive there would never be a council. They cited the examples of earlier councils; they cited several Pontifical laws by which they demonstrated that if I and my followers refused to call a council, the right of invoking one devolved upon them. And in fact, they said, if the other princes were in league with me, the duty of convoking a council belonged to the Roman Emperor, who once was the only one to summon them, and to the King of France, from his pre-eminence.[77]

PETER: Did they write scurrilous things about you then?

JULIUS: No, in fact the wretches were shrewder in this matter than I liked. They handled this most hateful business with marvelous moderation, and they not only refrained from curses, but they never addressed me without an honorific

preface, asking and beseeching by all things sacred and pious
that I should preside over the council when it was convoked,
620 as was proper for me, and as I had promised by oath, and that
I should devote my energy, together with them, to healing the
ills of the Church. I can't tell you how much ill will this
moderation of theirs generated against me,[78] especially since
they seasoned all their pronouncements with Sacred Scripture;
for it appears that a number of scholars were included among
them for that very purpose. Meanwhile they added fasts,
prayers, and a marvelously frugal life, in order to put me under
greater pressure by their reputation for holiness.[79]

PETER: Now you, for your part, on what grounds did you convoke your council?

JULIUS: By far the most splendid grounds. I revealed that my
intention was to reform, first, the head of the Church, that is
630 myself; then Christian princes; then the people as a whole.[80]

PETER: A fine comedy this is! But now I'm waiting for the cli-
max. I'd like to hear what those theologians decreed in their
Satan's convention.

JULIUS: Unworthy, abominable things. My mind shrinks from
recalling them.

PETER: Were they as unspeakable as all that?

JULIUS: Absolutely impious, sacrilegious, worse than heretical;
if I had not resisted them hand and foot, or rather with arms
as well as genius, the dignity of the Christian Church would
have been all finished.

PETER: Now I'm all the more curious to hear what they were.

JULIUS: I shudder to say it! The scoundrels proposed to recall
640 the Church, now flourishing in such wealth and power, to the
squalor and wretched frugality of its early days; that Cardinals,
who nowadays surpass any tyrants in high living, should be
reduced to poverty; that bishops should live on a much more
limited scale, supporting fewer attendants and fewer horses.

They decreed that Cardinals should not at will swallow up bishoprics, abbacies, priesthoods. So that no one man might possess several bishoprics, they voted to suppress those who, by hook or by crook as they say, accumulate hundreds of priesthoods if they can, so they would be content with such property as is sufficient for a frugal priest; that no one should be made supreme Pontiff or bishop or priest by the use of money, or in consideration of favoritism or toadying, but only through a worthy life; and if it were found to be otherwise, he should instantly be removed; that it would be lawful to drive from his office a Roman Pope who was manifestly criminal; that whoremongering and drunken bishops could be deprived of their posts; that priests who were manifestly criminal would have not only their priesthood but also a limb of their body removed from them; and many others things of the same kind —it would be revolting to recall them all. But they were all directed to the same end, that of burdening us with sanctimoniousness and stripping us of our wealth and power.[81]

PETER: Well then, what provisions were made against these evils in your sacrosanct Roman council?

JULIUS: I guess you have forgotten what I said, that I didn't want to accomplish anything by that pretended council except to "drive a nail with a nail." The first convocation was spent on certain solemn ceremonies that have the sanction of tradition, and I decided to observe them on account of their antiquity at any rate, although they are a waste of time; two rites were celebrated, one for the Holy Cross and one for the Holy Spirit, as if the business were being conducted by His inspiration; then a speech was recited, full of my praises. At the next session, as mightily as possible, I hurled the thunderbolt against those schismatic Cardinals, stating that whatever they had already deliberated on or were preparing to deliberate on was worse than impious, worse than sacrilegious, worse than heretical. At the third session, I terrified France by the same thunderbolt, transferring the marketplaces from Lyon, and explicitly excepting certain parts of France, to cause a further break between the people and the King, and to stimulate some revolutionary activity among them. And as soon as these measures had been taken, so they might have greater force by being proclaimed officially through Bulls, I informed all the princes, especially those I saw inclining to my side.[82]

PETER: And nothing was done except that?

JULIUS: What was done was what I wanted; I have won, provided my decrees will continue to have force. Those three Cardinals who persisted in their enterprise I stripped of their office in public ceremonies; I bestowed the revenue of their priesthoods on others, so that they won't easily be restored; themselves I consigned to Satan, and I would more gladly have consigned them to the stake if they had fallen into my hands.[83]

PETER: And yet, if what you are telling me is true, the decrees of that schismatic convention seem in no small degree holier than those of your sacrosanct council. I see nothing that has emerged from that except tyrannical threats, curses, and cruelty mixed with cunning. If Satan was responsible for that other convention, he appears to approach closer to Christ than whatever the spirit was that guided your council.

JULIUS: You had better watch out what you're saying! In all my Bulls I have cursed all those, whoever they may be, who supported that convention in any manner whatever.

PETER: Wretch, how he still breathes the spirit of that old Julius! But tell me now, what was the outcome of this affair?

JULIUS: That was the state of things when I left. Fortune will see how it comes out.

PETER: The schism remains, then?

JULIUS: It remains, and in fact is a great danger.

70

PETER: And you, the Vicar of Christ, preferred a schism to a true council?

JULIUS: Hundreds of schisms even, rather than agree to be degraded and forced to render an account of my whole life.

PETER: You know yourself too well, eh?

JULIUS: What business is it of yours?

PETER: I understand—it was not in your interest for that particular Camarina to be moved.[84] But which side will have the victory?

JULIUS: That is in the hand of Fortune; although there is more money on our side. The French are exhausted now by long wars;[85] the English still have untouched mountains of gold.[86] One thing I can predict with certainty: if the French win, God forbid, the designations will be reversed. That sacrosanct council will become the convention of Satan, and I a shadow of a Pope, not a Pope; the Holy Spirit will be on their side, and we will have done everything through the spirit of Satan. But I have great confidence, because of all the money I left, that this will not be the case.

PETER: But, tell me, what happened that turned you against the French and their King, whom your predecessors honored with the title of "Most Christian"?[87] Especially since you admit it was by their aid that you were kept alive, and also raised to that more than imperial crown of yours, and furthermore recovered Bologna and other cities, and conquered the Venetians, whom no one else had ever conquered. How was the memory of so many recent favors obliterated? How were so many alliances torn up?

JULIUS: To unfold that story would take a very long time. But, just to hit the high points, nothing that I did was done hastily; what my mind had long been pregnant with, I then began to give birth to. What I had previously concealed when the situation required it, I then brought into the open. I never really

71

loved the French, and that is the solemn truth. No Italian really loves barbarians; no more so, by Hercules, than a wolf loves lambs.[88] But I, who am not only an Italian, but actually a Genoese, used them as friends for just so long as I needed their services, since up to that point one may take advantage of barbarians. Meanwhile, I put up with many things,

730   I pretended many things, I invented many things. In short, there was nothing that I did not do or put up with. But when things had reached just the joint at which I wanted them, it remained for me to act the true Julius and remove all that barbarian scum from Italy.

PETER: What sort of beasts are these that you call barbarians?

JULIUS: They're human beings.

PETER: Human beings then, but not Christians?

JULIUS: Christians too, but what has that to do with it?

PETER: They actually are Christians then, but they lead an uncivilized life without laws and without culture?

740   JULIUS: No, in fact they are especially flourishing in those things; and furthermore, in what we envy them for most of all, wealth.

PETER: So what does the designation "barbarian" mean? What are you muttering?

GENIUS: I'll speak for him. Although the Italians are a hodgepodge conglomeration of barbarian nations, no more than dregs really, nevertheless they have swallowed this crazy idea from pagan literature, that they call men born outside Italy barbarians. And this designation among them is more insulting than if you called someone a parricide or church-robber.

750   PETER: So it seems. And yet, since Christ died for all men, and there is in Him no respect for persons, why didn't you embrace all men in the same spirit, when Christ himself did not discriminate among them?

JULIUS: Believe me, I would be eager to embrace Indians, Africans, Ethiopians, and Greeks, as long as they pay cash and acknowledge their leader by their taxes. But we've done a good job of cutting all these people down to size, most recently the Greeks,[89] because they were too stubborn and not willing enough to acknowledge the majesty of the Roman Pope.

PETER: So the Roman See is more or less the whole world's warehouse.

JULIUS: Is it such a big thing for us to reap the rewards of the flesh universally, when we sow spiritual seeds universally?

PETER: What spiritual seeds do you mean? I haven't heard anything so far except things of this world. Perhaps you draw them to Christ by sacred teaching?

JULIUS: Oh, there are men who may harangue them if they wish, and we don't prevent them, as long as they don't say anything against our majesty.

PETER: Well, what then?

JULIUS: What then? Why do kings get whatever they demand, except that individuals bring them whatever of their possessions the kings like, even if they get nothing in return? And so, whatever is sacred anywhere is to be attributed to us, even if we snore away our whole life. Although, beyond that, we very generously bestow indulgences for trivial sums; in the weightiest matters we grant dispensations for sums not very great; and we bless everyone who encounters us anywhere— that we do for *nothing*.[90]

PETER: I don't follow any of this. But return to what we started. Why does your holiest majesty shudder so at barbarians that you considered it worth scrambling together heaven and earth[91] in order to drive them from Italy?

JULIUS: I'll tell you. They're superstitious. Every barbarian nation is, but especially the French. As far as the Spaniards are concerned, they're not so alien to us, either in language or in way of life; but I wanted them out of the way too, so it would be possible for us once and for all to do as we wanted.

PETER: Do they worship other gods as well as Christ?

73

JULIUS: No, in fact they worship Christ himself too earnestly. It is marvelous how these foolish men are still moved by ancient and long-forgotten words.

PETER: You mean magic words?

JULIUS: Don't be silly. I mean simony, blasphemy, sodomy, sorcery, soothsaying.

PETER: Don't use such language!

JULIUS: Just as you now abominate them, so do they.

790 PETER: I won't talk about the words; but the things themselves —do they actually exist among you, or indeed among any Christians?

JULIUS: Naturally the barbarians themselves are not free of vices, but they suffer from different ones. They execrate ours and are indulgent with theirs; we in turn are indulgent with ours and abominate theirs. One thing we consider an abominable disgrace, to be avoided by any means fair or foul, is poverty; they consider it scarcely Christian to enjoy wealth, even when it has not been dishonestly come by.[92] We don't even dare to say the word drunkenness (in my attitude here I'm not so very different from them, though my position is consistent in the other matters); but the Germans consider it a little 800 foible, jolly rather than evil.[93] They strongly detest usurers;[94] but among us there is no class of men as necessary to the Church of Christ. They consider sexual perversion so foul that if anyone so much as mentions it they think the air and the sun are polluted; we like things the other way around.[95] Furthermore, as for simony, a word long since disappeared from the universe, they still dread its shadow, and they cling by their teeth to the antiquated laws of the ancients;[96] we look in another direction. And there are a good many other matters of this kind, in which we are not in harmony with the barbarians. Accordingly, since we are already so unlike in our way of life, they are to be kept 810 far away from our mysteries, which they will respect more if

they are ignorant of them. If they have once learned the secrets
of our Curia, they immediately divulge them, and somehow or
other they are exceedingly sharp-eyed in detecting vices. They
send the most derogatory letters back to their people. They
cry out that ours is not the See of Christ, but the dregs of
Satan. As for me, they debate whether, having achieved the
Pontificate as I did and living as I do, I am really to be considered Pope.[97] And in this way, they diminish first of all our
reputation for holiness, and then also our authority among men
who do not know us, who previously had heard nothing of us
except that we were the Vicar of Christ and held power next
to, and in fact equal to, that of God. And from these things
there arises an intolerable loss to the Christian Church. We sell
fewer dispensations and at a lower price; less revenue comes
in from bishoprics and priesthoods and abbacies; if anything
is exacted from the common people, they give it more grudg-
ingly. In short, business is worse everywhere, and the marketplaces produce less. Finally, they tremble less and less at our
thunderbolts. And if once they reach such a pitch of audacity
that they say the wicked Pope doesn't amount to anything,
and they have contempt for my thunderbolt and my threats,
our situation will surely be reduced to starvation. But if they
stay far away—such is the nature of barbarians—they will
venerate us more zealously, and we, by writing such letters as
the situation calls for, will keep them in line.

PETER: You're in pretty sorry shape if your apostolic authority
depends on men's being ignorant of your life and not knowing
about your "gimmicks." We wanted nothing more than that
everyone should know whatever we did, even in private; and
so we were held in the greatest esteem if men knew the truth
about us. But explain this to me: does the world now have
princes so religious, and is the reverence for priests among
them so great, that one and all will take up arms at the nod

of one man, and of such a one at that? In my time the worst
enemies we had to endure were princes.

JULIUS: As far as their life is concerned, it's not that they're such
840 superstitious Christians. In fact, they hold us in contempt and
regard us as a joke, except that some of the weaker ones among
them fear that terrible thunderbolt of excommunication to a
certain extent; still even these are moved not so much by the
thing itself as by how it will affect their reputation. Then
there are those who either covet our wealth or fear it, and on
that account they defer to our authority to a certain extent.
Some of them are firmly convinced that serious trouble is in
store for anyone who harasses even the lowliest priests. Almost
all of them, as they have been educated as laymen, attach some
importance to ceremonies, especially when we urge them to;
for ceremonies, like fairy tales, are aimed at the common
people. But we're talking about serious matters now. We
850 honor them with magnificent titles, even if they are utterly
evil, calling this one "Catholic," that one "Most Serene," another "Most Illustrious," another "August"; and we name all
of them "Beloved Sons." They in turn call us "Most Holy
Father" in their letters, and sometimes they submit to kissing
our feet. And when there is not much of importance involved,
they sometimes yield to our authority, in order to acquire for
themselves a reputation for piety among the people. We send
them consecrated roses, crowns, and swords, and we confirm
their dignity by mighty Bulls. They in turn send us horses,
soldiers, money, sometimes even boys;[98] and so, as the saying
goes, one mule scratches another.[99]

860 PETER: If that's the way they are, I still don't understand how
you were able to incite the greatest kings to very grave wars,
especially when you had to break so many alliances to do it.

JULIUS: If you can follow what I am going to say now, you will
recognize a genius greater than apostolic.

PETER: Well, I will try as hard as I can.

JULIUS: This was my major concern, to become thoroughly acquainted with the animating spirit, character, emotions, wealth, and strivings of all nations, and especially of all princes: who was at peace with whom, who had fallen out with whom; and then to make use of all these things for our own purposes. To begin with, we easily incited the French against the Venetians, because there was a long-standing, even ancient, rivalry between them. Besides we knew that France was eager to extend its rule, and the Venetians had occupied some of their cities too.[100] And so I made common cause with them. Then the Emperor, although he was not otherwise friendly to the French, since he had no other hope of recovering from the Venetians what they held (and they held a number of fine cities),[101] temporarily became an ally in this war. But at the same time, since it was not desirable that the French become too strong—and the thing had turned out better than I wanted —I began by inciting the King of Spain against them; in the first place, he was not a man of rock-hard faith, and besides it was very important to him that the power of the French be suppressed by any means, for a great many reasons but most of all so that he might never be shut off from his Neapolitan realm.[102] In addition to this, although I didn't like to, I pretended to receive the Venetians back into favor, in order to turn them loose against the French also, while they were still suffering from the grief of their recent disaster.[103] And then I alienated the Emperor from the French, to whom I had recently allied him;[104] partly by money, which is always the strongest argument to a man in need; and partly by renewing through letters and nuncios his long-standing hatred of the French (it's amazing how avidly that man always hated them), even though he had no chance to get revenge. Now, as for the English, I knew that they felt an instinctive hatred of the

77

890 French people, as well as of the Scots who were so closely joined to the French.[105] Furthermore I knew that they were a fierce and warlike nation, especially when there was hope of plunder. Then too, they were ever so slightly religious—because they were farthest from Rome. Finally they were cocky and almost riotous because of their new-found liberty, which they had finally acquired at the death of the most severe of kings,[106] so that they could now easily be incited to any madness—and to what I most wanted. Also to my advantage was their very young king, a boy rather, who had recently acquired the royal power and was of a fierce and lively and thoroughly youthful temper, that is restless and belligerent; he was ambitious for

900 more reasons than just his youth, and had his sights set on great things. And he was said from his earliest years to have intended to attack the French. Above all, he was related by marriage to the King of Spain, whom I had already drawn into the conflict.[107] All these circumstances I made use of for the advantage of the Church; and by hundreds of letters written not without genius I finally involved these princes in the gravest war of all. And I did not fail to approach all the other kings as well—the King of Hungary, the King of Portugal, and the Duke of Burgundy, who is the peer of kings.[108] But since they were not concerned in any of these matters, I was unable to coerce them. And yet I was well aware that if those others were involved in conflict, no one else would be at

910 peace. Well then, although they did our bidding for their own purposes, nevertheless they received the most honorable titles from us, so that the greater the disaster they brought to Christian peoples, the more religiously did they seem to be protecting the Church of God. And—so you may be even more amazed at either my genius, or maybe at my good luck—at that time the King of Spain was waging war with the Turks, with incredible success and very great profit, and yet, dropping

all that, he turned all his forces against the French.[109] In addition to this, the Emperor had been bound to the French not only by many treaties but also by very great favors, because at their expense and through their cooperation he had recovered his cities in Italy.[110] And he had reason to be concerned there: namely, to protect his property, as Padua had already defected; and also in Burgundy, namely so that he might protect his grandson, the Prince of Burgundy, from the Gelderlanders, who were very weighty enemies, because he had been responsible for inciting war against them.[111] And yet I succeeded in causing him to drop his own business and attend to mine. Next, there is no nation where the authority of the supreme Pontiff is less strong than in England (as will be very clear to anyone who examines the life of the divine Thomas, Bishop of Canterbury, and the Constitutions of their kings of long ago).[112] Nevertheless that nation, at other times very unwilling to put up with extortion, suffered itself to be practically flayed. It is amazing also how even the priests, who had become accustomed to withholding from us whatever they could, were induced by me to pay the required tribute to the King, little realizing what an opening they were making for kings in the future; but, on the other hand, neither did the kings themselves fully observe what a precedent they were establishing against themselves, namely that it would be possible thereafter for the holy man in Rome to remove from the royal power any prince that he objected to. The young King approached the business with greater force than I intended or had ordered; still, I preferred for him to overstep in that direction.[113] Well now, it would take a long time for me to explain point by point the devices by which I incited those princes to such a perilous war against Christians—princes whom no Pope had ever been able to arouse even against the Turks.

79

940 PETER: But it could happen that the flames of war you've ignited may in the end engulf the whole world.

JULIUS: All right, let them—as long as the Roman See keeps the dignity and the possessions that belong to it. But at that I have made an effort to cast the whole burden of the war away from Italians and onto the barbarians. Let them battle it out as much as they please; we will look on and perhaps profit by their madness.

PETER: Is this the right attitude for a shepherd and a Most Holy Father and the Vicar of Christ?

JULIUS: Well, why did they cause the schism?

PETER: But sins are sometimes to be endured, if greater evils
950 arise from their remedy. Besides, if you had allowed the council, there definitely would have been no place for a schism.

JULIUS: Don't talk like that! I would prefer hundreds of wars to a council. What if they had removed me from the Pontificate as a simoniac and a Pontifical trafficker, not a Pope? What if they had investigated my whole life and revealed their findings to the people?

PETER: Even if you were the legitimate Pope, still it would be better for you to resign the office rather than maintain your dignity if it meant the ruin of the Christian world; if indeed a bishopric bestowed upon an unworthy man is a dignity—in fact not even bestowed, but purchased and occupied by force. For
960 that reason, incidentally, it occurs to me that there was divine plan in your becoming the bane of the French, who were responsible for raising you in the first place to your position as the bane of the Church.

JULIUS: By my triple crown I swear, and by my most renowned triumphs, if you make me angry, you—even you—will feel the might of Julius.

PETER: Madman! Up to this moment all I hear about is a leader not of the Church but of this world, not just of this world but pagan, in fact more wicked than the pagans. Your boasts are that you were supreme in rupturing alliances, in igniting wars, in being responsible for the slaughter of human beings. That is the power of Satan, not of a Pope. That man who makes himself Vicar of Christ must approach as near as possible to His likeness. He has the greatest power, but combined with the greatest goodness; He has the greatest wisdom, but the simplest. In you I see the picture of power coupled with the maximum of malice and the maximum of stupidity. Now if the prince of evil, the devil, should wish to appoint a vicar for himself, whom would he choose but one like you? Tell me, where have you acted like an apostolic man?

JULIUS: What is more apostolic than to enlarge the Church of Christ?

PETER: But if the Church is the Christian people, bound together by the spirit of Christ, I would say that you have subverted the Church by provoking the whole world to horrible wars, so that you could be evil and pestilent with impunity.

JULIUS: What *we* mean by the Church is sacred buildings, priests, and especially the Roman Curia; above all, myself, the head of the Church.

PETER: But Christ made us servants, Himself the head, unless now a second head has grown out. But tell me, in what ways has the Church been enlarged?

JULIUS: Now you're getting to the point; so I'll tell you. That Church, once starving and poor, is flourishing now with all sorts of adornments.

PETER: How? In intensity of faith?

JULIUS: There you go talking nonsense again.

PETER: In sacred learning?

JULIUS: You slay me.

PETER: In contempt for the world?

JULIUS: Let me speak. I mean in real adornments; you're talking about mere words.

PETER: Well, what *do* you mean then?

JULIUS: I mean royal palaces, beautiful horses and mules, plenty of servants, well-trained troops, the choicest of retinues—

GENIUS: Gorgeous whores, the most accommodating of pimps.

JULIUS: —gold, purple, revenue; so that there is no king that would not seem lowly and poor compared to the wealth and pomp of the Roman Pope; no one so ambitious that he would not acknowledge himself surpassed; no one so luxurious that he would not deplore his own meanness; no one with so much money, even a loan shark, who would not envy our wealth. And I tell you, these adornments I have maintained, and I have added to them.

PETER: But do tell me, who was the very first to sully and burden, with those adornments of yours, the Church which Christ intended to be perfectly pure and at the same time perfectly unencumbered?

JULIUS: What does that have to do with it? At least—and this is the main point—we have them, we own them, and we enjoy them. But—all right; they say that somebody or other named Constantine unloaded the entire majesty of his empire on Sylvester, the Roman Pope: trappings, horses, chariots, his helmet, sword belt, cloak, entourage, swords, golden crowns (of the purest gold, incidentally), armies, artillery, cities, kingdoms.

PETER: And are there reliable documents attesting to this largesse?

JULIUS: Nothing except one codicil included among the decretals.[114]

PETER: It could be a legend.

JULIUS: Actually, I've suspected that myself. What sane man would give up such a magnificent empire even to his Father? But, nonetheless, it is greatly to my advantage to believe it, and as for the busybodies who try to refute it, we have enjoined utter silence on them by means of threats.

PETER: Well—I still don't hear anything that isn't worldly.

JULIUS: Perhaps you are still dreaming of that old Church, in which you and a few starveling bishops ran a really frigid Pontificate, subject to poverty, sweat, dangers, and a thousand nuisances. Time has changed everything for the better. The Roman Pope is now quite a different thing; you were Pope in name and title only. What if you could see today so many sacred buildings erected by kingly wealth, so many thousands of priests everywhere (many of them very rich), so many bishops equal to the greatest kings in military power and in wealth, so many splendid palaces belonging to priests; and especially if you could see today in Rome so many Cardinals dressed in purple with regiments of servants crowding around them, so many horses better than those of a king, so many mules decorated with linen, gold, and jewels, some of them even shod in gold and silver? But then, if you caught sight of the supreme Pontiff being carried high in the air in a golden chair by soldiers, and everyone worshiping him all along the way as he waves his hand; if you could hear the booming of cannon, the noise of horns, the blare of trumpets, if you could see the flash of artillery, hear the applause of the people, their shouting, see everything glowing in torchlight, and even the most powerful princes having difficulty being admitted to kiss the blessed feet; if you could have seen that Roman priest using his foot to place the golden crown on the Emperor, who is the king of all kings (that is if written laws have any force), even though all he retains is the shadow of a mighty name: then, I say, if you had seen and heard all this[115]—what would you say?

PETER: That I was looking at a tyrant worse than worldly, an enemy of Christ, the bane of the Church.

JULIUS: You would say otherwise if you had witnessed even one of my triumphs, for example, the one at which I was carried into Bologna, or the one I celebrated at Rome for the

defeat of the Venetians, or the one at which I was carried back
into Rome after escaping from Bologna; or the last one I had
1050   here, when the French were routed, completely unexpectedly,
at Ravenna. The ponies, the horses, the parade of armed
soldiers, the adornments of the commanders, the sight of the
choice boys, the torches glowing everywhere, the lavishness of
the displays that were carried by, the procession of bishops, the
proud Cardinals, the trophies, the booty, the shouts of the
people and the soldiers resounding to heaven, everything ring-
ing with applause, the music of trumpets, the blast of horns,
the flashing of cannon, the coins scattered among the people,
and myself carried aloft like some divine thing, the leading
figure and the one responsible for the whole show—if you had
seen all this, then you would have said that the Scipios, the
Aemilii, the Augusti were miserable cheapskates compared to
me.

1060 PETER: Hah! Enough about your triumphs, most glorious
soldier![116] The fact is, I find those men appealing, pagans
though they were, when I consider how I loathe you who, after
so many thousands of Christians were slaughtered in your be-
half, celebrated triumphs as the "Most Holy Father in Christ";
who stand as the one responsible for the destruction of so many
regiments; who gained for Christ not so much as one pitiful
soul, either by word or by the example of your life. By the
bowels of my Father! Oh, worthy Vicar of Christ—Christ who
gave Himself as an offering to save all men! You, to protect
one pestilential head, called down ruin on the whole world.

JULIUS: You say those things because you envy our glory, when
you see how lowly was your administration compared to ours.

1070 PETER: How dare you brazenly compare your glory with mine—
although my glory is Christ's glory, not my own? First of all,
if you grant me that Christ was the best and the true prince of
the Church, He himself gave me the keys of the kingdom of

heaven, He himself entrusted to me the pasturing of His sheep, He himself warranted my faith by His commendation. As for you, it was money, it was the exertions of mortal men, it was fraud that made you Pope; that is, if such a one is to be called Pope at all. I won so many thousands of souls for Christ; you dragged as many to ruin. I was the first to teach Rome about Christ, when it had been pagan; you arose to teach it about paganism, when it was already Christian. I healed the sick with just the shadow of my body;[117] I freed those who were beset by demons;[118] I recalled the dead to life;[119] and I filled every place in which I found myself with good works. Could anything comparable be said about your triumphs? I was able with a word to consign to Satan anyone I wished; Sapphira and her husband experienced how great my power was.[120] And yet, whatever power I had I extended for the benefit of all; you were useless to anyone, and if you had any power—in fact, even in matters where you lacked power—you turned it to the destruction of the people of the whole world.

JULIUS: I wonder why you don't also add these to the catalogue of your glories: poverty, vigils, sweat, judgments, dungeons, chains, revilement, blows, and, in the end, the cross.

PETER: You do right to remind me; I shall glory more justly in those things than in miracles. In the name of these, Christ bade us to rejoice and exult; in the name of these He called us blessed.[121] And so Paul, once my colleague, when he boasts of his deeds, does not recount cities captured by arms, nor legions cut down with the sword, nor the princes of the earth incited to war, nor tyrannical arrogance; but rather shipwrecks, chains, lashes, perils, snares.[122] This is the triumph truly apostolical, this is the glory of a Christian leader! He boasts of those whom he got for Christ, those whom he drew away from godlessness, not how many thousands of ducats he stacked up. Finally, as

1100 for us, now celebrating an eternal triumph with Christ, even the wicked pursue us with praises; as for you, there is no one who will not execrate you, unless he either resembles you or is a flatterer.

JULIUS: This is all new to me!

PETER: I suppose so; how would you have had leisure to leaf through the Gospels, to read and reread Paul's Epistles and mine, when you were occupied with so many embassies, alliances, schemes, armies, triumphs? Even the other arts prefer a mind free of sordid interests; but the discipline of Christ requires a heart completely cleansed of every taint of earthly 1110 concern. And such a master did not descend from heaven to earth to deliver any easy or common philosophy to mortals. It is not a relaxing or a carefree profession to be a Christian. To spurn all pleasures like poison, to trample on wealth as if it were dirt, to consider life as nothing: this is the profession of a Christian man. Since these things appear intolerable to those who are not moved by the spirit of Christ, they turn away to empty words and mere ceremonies, and to a false head of Christ they add a false body.

JULIUS: Tell me, what good thing will you leave for me, if you deprive me of my money, despoil me of my kingdom, strip me of my income, swear me off pleasures, and, in the end, take away my life?

1120 PETER: Why not call Christ himself unhappy because, although He was universally supreme, He became an object of universal mockery? In poverty, sweat, fasting, thirst, and hunger He passed His whole life; and, in the end, He died by the most humiliating of all deaths.

JULIUS: Perhaps He will find someone to praise Him, but no one to imitate Him; not these days, at any rate.

PETER: And yet, in the final analysis, this very praise constitutes imitation. Still, Christ does not deprive His followers of good

86

things; rather He enriches them with true and eternal goods in place of false ones. But He enriches none who has not first renounced all the goods of this world and been cleansed. As He himself was entirely celestial, so He wanted His body, that is the Church, to be as like Him as possible, that is completely remote from the taints of the world. Otherwise, how could it resemble Him who sits in heaven, if it is still immersed in the uncleanness of the earth? But when it has shaken free of all the possessions of this world, and also, what is more, of its wants, then at last Christ reveals His wealth; in exchange for honeyed pleasures, that are in fact tinged with much bitterness, He bestows a taste of the joys of heaven; in exchange for the wealth left behind, He bestows far more excellent wealth—

JULIUS: What wealth, I beg you?

PETER: —unless you regard as ordinary wealth the gift of prophecy, the gift of knowledge, the gift of miracles; unless you consider Christ himself lowly, when whoever possesses Him possesses within himself everything; in short, unless you consider that we here lead a poverty-stricken life. And so, the more afflicted a man is on earth, the more does he experience delight in Christ; the poorer a man is on earth, the richer he is in Christ; the more downcast on earth, the more elevated and honored in Him; the less he lives on earth, the more he lives in Christ. But while He wished the whole of His body to be perfectly pure, especially is this so of His ministers, that is bishops;[123] and among these the greater one is, the more he should resemble Christ, and the more he should be unencumbered and unburdened by any worldly possessions. Now, by contrast, I see the man who wants to be regarded as next to Christ and, in fact, equal to Him, submerged in the filthiest of all things by far: money, power, armies, wars, alliances— not to say anything at this point about his vices. But then, although you are as remote as possible from Christ, neverthe-

less you misuse the name of Christ for your own arrogant purposes; and under the pretext of Him who despised the kingdom
of the world, you act the part of a tyrant of the world; and,
although a true enemy of Christ, you take the honor due him.
You bless others, yourself accursed; to others you open heaven,
from which you yourself are locked out and kept far away;
you consecrate, and are execrated; you excommunicate, when
you have no communion with the saints. What difference is
there between you and the Sultan of the Turks, except that you
1160   make a show of the name of Christ? Certainly your minds are
the same, and the squalor of your lives is exactly alike. It is
you who are the greater bane to the earth.

JULIUS: But I always wanted the Church to be adorned with all
good things. They say that Aristotle established three categories of goods,[124] of which some come from fortune, some
from the body, and some from the mind. So I did not want to
reverse the order of goods; I began with the goods of fortune.
Perhaps I would gradually have reached the goods of the mind
if a premature death had not snatched me from the earth.

PETER: Premature indeed—and you a septuagenarian![125] Still,
why did you need to mix water with fire?[126]

1170 JULIUS: Well, if those benefits are lacking, the people won't
give a hoot for us; even as it is they fear and hate us. So the
whole Christian state would collapse if it could not protect
itself against the power of its enemies.

PETER: On the contrary, if the Christian peoples saw in you the
true gifts of Christ—namely, holiness of life, sacred learning,
burning love, prophecy, virtues—the more they thought you
were cleansed of worldly goods, the more they would admire
you; and the Christian state would flourish more widely if it
were a source of wonder to the world through its contempt for
pleasures, for wealth, for power, and for death. As it is now,
1180   not only has it been very narrowly constricted, but, if you

examine the matter closely, you will even find that many Christians are that in name only. I ask you, when you were the supreme shepherd of the Church, didn't you ever reflect privately on how the Church was born, how it grew, how it became established? It wasn't by wars, by wealth, by horses, was it? No, it was by suffering, by the blood of the martyrs and by ours, by dungeons, by lashes. You say that the Church has been enlarged, when its ministers are burdened by earthly sway; you call it adorned, when it is sullied by worldly rewards and delights; you call it defended, when, to protect the property of priests, the whole world is embroiled in the most destructive wars; you describe it as flourishing, when it is drunk with worldly pleasures; peaceful, when, with no voice raised in protest, it enjoys wealth—vices, rather. And on these grounds you have deceived the princes: they have learned their lesson from your example, and they call their grand robberies and mad conflicts "the defense of Christ."

JULIUS: No one has ever talked to me like that before!

PETER: What did you learn, then, from your orators?

JULIUS: From them I used to hear nothing but unadulterated praises; with their verbal trappings they thundered in celebration of me; they proclaimed me Jupiter who shakes everything with his thunderbolt; they proclaimed me a kind of true divinity, the salvation of the people of the earth, and a great many other things like that.[127]

PETER: It's no wonder at all that there was no one who could season you, since you were the salt that has lost its savor,[128] and a fool. For the proper gift of an apostolic man is to teach others Christ, and to do it with perfect purity.

JULIUS: So you won't open, then?

PETER: To anyone sooner than to such a pestilence. Anyway, as far as you're concerned, we are all excommunicated. But do you want some pretty good advice? You have a gang of vigorous men; you have money beyond counting; you yourself are a great builder:[129] build yourself a new Paradise—but fortify it well, so that it can't be captured by evil demons.

JULIUS: No, rather I shall do what befits me—I shall wait a few months and, when I have built up my forces, knock you out of there, unless you come out to surrender. For I have no doubt that within a short time scores of thousands of men will be butchered in battle and join with me.

PETER: Oh, ruinous thing! Oh, pitiful Church! Hey, Genius— I prefer talking with you rather than with that foul monster.

GENIUS: What can I do for you?

PETER: Are other bishops like him?

GENIUS: A good part of them are of the same stuff; but this one is the standard bearer for them all.

PETER: Was it you who drove the man to so many crimes?

GENIUS: I? Not at all. In fact he was so far ahead of me that I could hardly keep up with him even though I have the help of wings.

PETER: Well, I don't wonder that so few come to this place, when pestilences like this sit at the helm of the Church; but I have an idea that the people at any rate can be cured, and the reason is that they honor this filthy sewer simply because he bears the title of Pope.

GENIUS: Precisely so. But my master has been gesturing at me and shaking his stick. So farewell!

Notes to Introduction
and on the Text
by J. Kelley Sowards

Notes to Introduction

1. Both the introduction and text of the present work are heavily in the debt of P. S. Allen's monumental *Opus Epistolarum Des. Erasmi Roterodami,* 12 vols. (Oxford: The Clarendon Press, 1906-58), hereafter cited as Allen, *Ep. Eras.;* and Wallace K. Ferguson (ed.), *Erasmi Opuscula, A Supplement to the Opera Omnia* (The Hague: Martinus Nijhoff, 1933), hereafter cited as Ferguson, *Opuscula.* To those two works we owe our knowledge of the editions of the work, the solution to the problem of its authorship, and, to Ferguson, the establishment of the critical Latin text from which this edition was prepared.

2. The approximate date, if not the precise edition, is suggested by both Allen, *Ep. Eras.,* II, Ep. 502, intro. p. 419 and Ferguson, *Opuscula,* pp. 41-42.

3. In *ibid.,* pp. 41-42, Ferguson comments, "A number of editions followed in rapid succession, almost all without indication of place or date. . . . but there is no way of absolutely identifying these editions"; and pp. 62-63, "It is exceedingly difficult, if not impossible, to arrange the undated editions of the *Iulius* in chronological order with any degree of certainty. The first twelve editions probably all appeared within a very short time, though some may be later than ed. B, dated 1521." For contemporary references to the *Julius,* see Allen, *Ep. Eras.,* II, Ep. 532, pp. 475-76; II, Ep. 543, p. 494; III, Ep. 622, p. 45; III, Ep. 636, p. 58; III, Ep. 785, p. 239; III, Ep. 849, p. 342; III, Ep. 852, p. 348; III, Ep. 877, p. 415; III, Ep. 908, pp. 463-64; as well as the more complete list in *ibid.* II, Ep. 502, intro. p. 419 and in Ferguson, *Opuscula,* p. 53.

4. For the reports on the hostility to the book in Cologne which were received or noted by Erasmus, see Allen, *Ep. Eras.*, III, Ep. 622, p. 45; III, Ep. 636, p. 58; III, Ep. 785, p. 239; and III, Ep. 908, pp. 463-64.

5. *Ibid.*, III, Ep. 852, p. 348, from Dorp in Louvain, July 14, 1518. See also *The Correspondence of Sir Thomas More,* ed. Elizabeth F. Rogers (Princeton: Princeton University Press, 1947), Ep. 83, pp. 188-98, in which More comments rather extensively upon Dorp's hostile reaction to the book.

6. Allen, *Ep. Eras.*, II, Ep. 532, pp. 475-76 and intro. p. 475.

7. Probably commenting upon the letter from Morillon, cited in n. 6 among other reports, Erasmus writes, "Dialogus ille Iulii et Petri, ut intelligo, iam τῷ καγκελλαρίῳ μεγάλῳ in manibus est et unice placet," *ibid.*, II, Ep. 543, p. 494.

8. *Ibid.*, III, Ep. 849, p. 342.

9. *Ibid.*, III, Ep. 636, p. 58; and Ep. 961, pp. 574-75.

10. In *ibid.*, III, Ep. 622, p. 45, Erasmus writes to John Caesarius, August 16, 1517, "Audieram iampridem huiusmodi fabulam actam in Gallia, ubi talium nugarum immodica licentia semper fuit. Eam, opinor, aliquis in Latinum sermonem transtulit;" and in the previously cited letter to the Count of Neuenahr, *ibid.*, III, Ep. 636, p. 58, ". . . actum inibi regalibus festis, quibus solenne est huiusmodi naeniis lascivire scholasticis." In his long letter "To a Monk" Thomas More, defending his friend Erasmus against the charge of having written the *Julius,* echoes this view, ". . . rem Parisiis ludis actam publicis," *The Correspondence of Sir Thomas More,* Ep. 83, pp. 188-89. Allen, *Ep. Eras.*, III, Ep. 961, p. 547, n. suggests that Erasmus was referring to a specific play, one by Pierre Gringore, called *L'Homme obstiné.*

11. In his "Letter to a Monk," More says, "As many people know, the Reverend Father Poncher, Bishop of Paris and former Legate to our country, has ascribed the work to Faustus," Elizabeth F. Rogers (ed.), *St. Thomas More: Selected Letters* (New Haven and London: Yale University Press, 1961), Ep. 26 (83), p. 121. See also the Latin text in *The Correspondence of Sir Thomas More,* Ep. 83, pp. 188-89.

12. This view was so prevalent that "One of the earliest editions, probably printed in Paris, bears the title, F[austi] A[ndrelini] F[orliuiensis], Poete Regii, libellus . . . ," Ferguson, *Opuscula,* pp. 46-47. The existence of this edition led many others to attribute the work to Faustus, including Ludwig von Pastor, *The History of the Popes from the Close of the Middle Ages.,* ed. F. I. Antrobus (Lon-

don and St. Louis: Routledge and Kegan Paul Ltd. and B. Herder Book Co., 1950), VI, 437-38, n. This is also the case with David Friedrich Strauss, *Ulrich von Hutten his Life and Times,* trans. Mrs. G. Sturge (London: Daldy, Isbister and Co., 1874), p. 53. But the definitive judgment on the question of Faustus' authorship belongs to the German scholar Ludwig Geiger who carefully analyzes the whole question in "Studien zur Geschichte des französischen Humanismus," *Vierteljahrsschrift für Kultur und Litteratur der Renaissance,* I (1886), especially 17 ff., and concludes (pp. 29-30) that the *Julius* was not written by Faustus.

Charles Oulmont, *Pierre Gringore* (Paris: Librairie spéciale pour l'histoire de France, 1911), pp. 226-37, in discussing the flood of anti-papal writings sanctioned by the French court, mentions "un Epistre de la Reine Anne au Roi, écrite en vers latins par Fauste Andrelin. . . ." which was strongly anti-papal. Perhaps this, as well as other specific pieces, suggested Faustus as the author of the *Julius* to contemporaries. Certainly it must have lent color to the suggestion.

Erasmus helped the argument along by including among the speculations he wrote to Cardinal Campeggio, May 1, 1519, the rumor: "rursus alii Fausto poetae tribuebant. . . ." Allen, *Ep. Eras.,* III, Ep. 961, p. 575.

13. Once more it is Erasmus reporting the current rumors, in the same righteously indignant letter to Campeggio, "alii Hieronymo Balbo." And he adds piously, "Ego quid de his [the anonymous Spaniard, Faustus, or Balbi] coniectem non habeo," *ibid.,* III, Ep. 961, p. 575. Apparently this attribution to Balbi was widely accepted. Pastor, *op. cit.,* vi, 437-38 n. refers to this reference of Erasmus' and adds: "The anonymous translator of this Dialogue (Julius II. Ein Gespräch vor der Himmelsthüre; translated from [*N.B.*] the Latin of G. Balbi. Berlin, 1877) attributes it without any proof to the Bishop of Gurk, while Balbi's biographer, Retzer, concludes his examination with *non liquet.*" Again, however, the careful arguments of Geiger prevail on the question of Balbi's authorship. See Geiger, *op. cit.,* pp. 27-28.

14. See Allen, *Ep. Eras.,* I, Ep. 23, p. 105, n.; Augustin Renaudet, *Préréforme et Humanisme à Paris pendent les Guerres d'Italie (1494-1517)* (Paris: E. Champion, 1916), p. 121; and P. S. Allen, "Hieronymus Balbus in Paris," *English Historical Review,* LXVII (1902), 417-28.

15. Ferguson, *Opuscula,* pp. 47-48 points out that while the dia-

logue has certainly been attributed to Hutten, "there is no external evidence to support this opinion, and a careful comparison of the satire with Hutten's epigrams on Julius brings to light no indication of common authorship." See the standard Strauss, *op. cit.,* pp. 43 ff, 47 ff, 53, 83-84, and 216 ff. See also Geiger, *op. cit.,* p. 19, n. 2.

16. Allen, *Ep. Eras.* II, Ep. 532, p. 475, dated February 18, [1517]. Allen thinks that Morillon was only making a shrewd guess.

17. *Ibid.,* III, Ep. 636, p. 58. See also Epp. 622 and 785, pp. 45 and 239.

18. *Ibid.,* III, Ep. 908, pp. 463-64.

19. The quotation from the letter to Campeggio, *ibid.,* III, Ep. 961, pp. 574-75, dated May 1, 1519, is paralleled by the one to Wolsey, dated about two weeks later, *ibid.,* III, Ep. 967, pp. 592-93. Campeggio was persuaded, see *ibid.,* IV, Ep. 995, p. 5; but Wolsey apparently didn't bother to reply.

20. *The Correspondence of Sir Thomas More,* Ep. 83, pp. 188-89. See also, for the English translation, Rogers (ed.), *St. Thomas More: Selected Letters,* Ep. 26 (83), pp. 121-22.

21. While much of this correspondence is missing, the contention is borne out by Lupset's letter, Allen, *Ep. Eras.,* II, Ep. 431, p. 268.

22. Even in the normal course of things he had some basis for his suspicions. In Italy he had been sent by a casual acquaintance a volume of his own letters which had been collected quite without his knowledge. See Allen, *Ep. Eras.,* I, Ep. 216, p. 452, n. His *De Copia* had been pirated and published, some time before his own authorized edition, from a lost manuscript copy. See my article, "Erasmus and the Apologetic Textbook: A Study of the *De Duplici Copia Verborum ac Rerum," Studies in Philology,* LV (April, 1958), 122-23, and n. 4.

23. Allen, *Ep. Eras.,* II, Ep. 431, p. 268.

24. *Ibid.,* II, Ep. 502, p. 420. See the detailed analysis of this important letter in J. B. Pineau, "Erasme, est-il l'Auteur du 'Julius'?," *Revue de Littérature comparée,* V (1925), 391-93.

25. Ferguson, *Opuscula,* pp. 43-44. This interpretation is confirmed by Allen, *Ep. Eras.,* II, Ep. 502, intro. pp. 418-19. "The composition . . . is evidently the *Iulius Exclusus,* the third character in which is 'Iulii Genius.' From this direct statement of the existence of a copy written by Erasmus' own hand, there can be no doubt that he was the author of it."

26. *Ibid.,* II, Ep. 543, pp. 494-95.

27. See Ferguson, *Opuscula,* pp. 43-44 and Allen, *Ep. Eras.,* II, Ep. 502, intro. p. 419. Allen had seen two manuscript copies, ". . . by J. A. Brassicanus, 24 Aug. 1517 (Vienna MS 9846 ff. 16-59), and by the writer in the Munich MS (p. 35), 31 Dec. 1518," but he surmises that both were "probably made from printed books."

28. In *ibid.,* III, Ep. 664, pp. 89-90, we find Lupset writing again in some anxiety, hoping that Erasmus does not blame him for "the betrayal" of the manuscript into print; and Ferguson, *Opuscula,* p. 44 contends, "Erasmus, for his part, declared himself satisfied with the return of the manuscript the previous year and exonerated his young friend from all blame."

29. Both Allen, *Ep. Eras.,* II, Ep. 502, intro. p. 419 and Ferguson, *Opuscula,* pp. 55, 62-63 identify this Amerbach manuscript as the "first edition" of the work.

30. On October 19, [1518] Erasmus wrote to Capito that the work ". . . iam passim vulgatus est ac saepius excusus. O intemperias," Allen, *Ep. Eras.,* III, Ep. 877, p. 415. Allen notes that this is "a further indication that Erasmus' friends at Basel had seen the *Iulius* in MS. and probably were aware of his authorship."

31. *Ibid.,* IV, Ep. 1218, p. 541.

32. A few modern scholars still insist that the *Julius exclusus*—for all its provocative textual parallels and the web of circumstantial evidence that surrounds it—is not the work of Erasmus. The leading exponents of this view are Carl Stange, *Erasmus und Julius II: Eine Legende* (Berlin: A Töpelmann, 1937); Henri Hauser, "Le *Julius,* est-il d'Erasme?," *Revue de Littérature comparée,* VII (1927), 605-18; and P. Paschini, *L'autore del dialogo satirico contro Giulio II,* in *Atti dell'Accad. degli Arcadi,* 1933-34. Some Erasmian scholars still suspend judgment largely on the scrupulous point that until conclusive proof in the form of a verifiable text or unequivocal statement comes to light the case, no matter how good, is still circumstantial. This is true of Augustin Renaudet, *Préréforme et Humanisme à Paris,* p. 666 and n. 6 and *Erasme et l'Italie,* pp. 112-13. This is also the case with Cornelis Reedijk since the publication of his "Schimpdicht van Erasmus," *op. cit.,* p. 207, in spite of his earlier rejection of the case for Erasmian authorship.

But the vast majority of modern authorities now conclude that Erasmus was the author. The line of this argument goes back at least to John Jortin, *The Life of Erasmus* (London, 1768) who ascribes it to Erasmus (p. 595). A century later H. Durand de Laur, in his *Érasme, précurseur et initiateur de l'esprit moderne* (Paris, 1872) made the first modern "case" for attributing the book to Erasmus with an elaborate textual comparison with his other works. Weight was added to the case by the work of Ludwig Geiger, especially in his "Studien zur Geschichte des französischen Humanismus," *Vierteljahrsschrift für Kultur und Litterature der Renaissance,* V, I, no. 2 (1886), 1-48, which disposed convincingly of the Andrelinus and Hutten arguments; by J. B. Pineau, especially in his "Erasme, est-il l'auteur du *Julius?,*" *Revue de Littérature comparée,* V (1925), 394-96, 400 ff. which detailed the affinities between the *Julius* and other works of Erasmus both as regards style and content, and in *Erasme et la Papauté. Etude Critique du "Julius Exclusus"* (Paris: Les Presses universitaires de France, 1924), pp. 15 ff and 18 ff; by E. V. Telle, "Le 'De Copia Verborum' d'Erasme et le 'Julius Exclusus e Coelis,' " *Bibliotheque d'Humanisme et Renaissance,* XXII (1948), 441-47; and finally by the work of Allen and Ferguson.

In recent years Germain Marc'hadour in his *L'Univers de Thomas More* (Paris: Librairie Philosophique J. Vrin, 1963), p. 201, under the year 1513, has the entry, "Erasme rédige *Julius Exclusus,* dialogue où Saint Pierre 'exclut' Jules II du Paradis (imprimé c. 1517)"; and Giulio Vallese, *Da Dante ad Erasmo, Studi di letteratura umanistica* (Napoli: G. Scalabrini Editore, 1962), observes, in this penetrating essay on the *Colloquies,* of the "brillantissima satira" *Julius exclusus,* "Ma è impossibile oggi contestarne la paternità erasmiana," p. 135. Most recently Professor Roland H. Bainton has reviewed the evidence of authorship in an article, "Erasmus and Luther and the Dialog *Julius Exclusus,*" prepared for the Franz Laur *Festschrift,* in which he concludes (p. 3) ". . . after surveying all the evidence and after reading the dialog itself, one ends with the powerful impression that Erasmus had a major part in the composition even though another may have supplied some of the details." In addition to the strictly internal and external evidence heretofore cited, it might also be observed that every fact or prejudice expressed in the dialogue is one which Erasmus had opportunity to know or which we can substantiate as his. This includes both his information and—what is even more illuminating—his misinformation.

33. Both Ferguson and Allen are rather generous in Erasmus' cause on this point. Allen, *Ep. Eras.,* II, Ep. 502, intro. pp. 418-19, while

conclusively identifying him as the author, goes on to say, "although by many equivocal utterances—none of which is a direct denial—he attempted to conceal the fact." Ferguson, *Opuscula,* p. 42, writes, "Erasmus refused to acknowledge his responsibility for the dialogue, resorting to every form of equivocation short of literal mendacity."

34. Allen, *Ep. Eras.,* III, Ep. 622, p. 45. See also the adage "Ollas ostentare," which appeared in the 1515 edition of the *Adagia,* the passage in defence of the *Praise of Folly,* in which he says, "I satirised no one by name, and without disturbing that Camarina of vices and crimes, I dwelt briefly on points that are funny rather than vile," Margaret M. Phillips, *The 'Adages' of Erasmus,* pp. 356-57.

35. The dispensation is reproduced from papal registers in Allen, *Ep. Eras.,* III, Ep. 187ᴬ, pp. xxix-xxx. See also *ibid.,* II, Ep. 517, n. 7 and Albert Hyma, *The Youth of Erasmus* (Ann Arbor: University of Michigan Press, 1930), p. 53 and n.

36. This was conveyed in full-dress form to Andrea Ammonio, who was empowered to confer it upon Erasmus in a brief from Leo X, dated at Rome, January 26, 1517, and drafted by the papal secretary Sadoleto, Allen, *Ep. Eras.,* II, Ep. 517, pp. 433-36; and accompanied by an official notification to Erasmus himself from the pope, *ibid.,* II, Ep. 518, pp. 436-37, as well as a short and cordial personal note, *ibid.,* II, Ep. 519, p. 438. See also *ibid.,* I, Ep. 226, p. 466 and n.

37. Ferguson, *Opuscula,* pp. 44-45.

38. This is the conclusion of both Ferguson, *ibid.,* pp. 41-42 and Allen, *Ep. Eras.,* II, Ep. 502, intro. p. 419. If nothing else the occasional nature of the piece would tend to pinpoint the time.

39. The Italian correspondence is sparse, in all no more than a dozen letters. See *ibid.,* I, Epp. 200-213. There is a gap in the sequence of letters from May 27, 1509, to April 10, 1511, for which period there is virtually no substantive biographical material. See my article in *Studies in the Renaissance,* IX (1962), 161-86. At the very time when reports of the pope's death would have reached England there is a gap in the correspondence of more than six months. See Allen, *Ep. Eras.,* I, Ep. 270, intro. p. 526 and Epp. 269, 270.

40. The translated passage is from F. M. Nichols (ed. and trans.), *The Epistles of Erasmus from his Earliest Letters to his Fifty-First Year* (London: Longmans, Green and Co., 1901-18), I, Ep. 110, pp. 225-26, hereafter cited as Nichols, *Letters.*

41. Allen, *Ep. Eras.,* I, Ep. 267, p. 519, n.; Ep. 192, pp. 423-24;

Ep. 197, pp. 429-30; Ep. 200, pp. 431-32; Ep. 205, pp. 434-35; Ep. 207, pp. 437-39; Ep. 209, pp. 440-42; the Erasmian biographical letter of Beatus Rhenanus in *ibid.,* I, p. 55; and Appendix VI, pp. 590-93. See also Karl Schätti, *Erasmus von Rotterdam und die Römische Kurie* (Basel und Stuttgart: Verlag von Helbing und Lichtenhahn, 1954), and Ambroise Firmin-Didot, *Alde Manuce et l'Hellenisme à Venise* (Paris: Typographie d'Ambroise Firmin-Didot, 1875), pp. 148-49, 452-53.

42. That his reception in Italy marked an epoch in Erasmus' life is the conclusion of most authorities. See Margaret M. Phillips, *Erasmus and the Northern Renaissance* (London: The English Universities Press, Ltd., 1959), p. 61; Pierre de Nolhac, *Erasme et l'Italie* (Paris: Les Cahiers de Paris, 1925), pp. 16-17; Renaudet, *Erasme et l'Italie,* p. xi; and Deno John Geanakoplos, *Greek Scholars in Venice* (Cambridge: Harvard University Press, 1962), pp. 256-78.

43. Margaret M. Phillips, *The 'Adages' of Erasmus,* pp. 104-5, makes a special point of this in speaking of the influence of his Italian experiences as reflected in his work on the *Adagia* between 1509 and 1512. In particular she speaks of "that strange essay *Scarabeus aquilam quaerit,*" observing, "Who then was the prototype of the ruthless Eagle? Perhaps we must look to Italy for it, to the type of the Renaissance prince whose features become clear in the pages of Machiavelli, and particularly to the ecclesiastical tyrant whom Erasmus had studied at first hand and whom he cordially hated, Julius II. . . . The most striking parts of the whole book were the diatribes against war, not only in the long *Dulce bellum inexpertis* and *Spartam nactus es, hanc orna,* but in occasional passages scattered through the notes. It was Julius II who turned Erasmus into a pacifist."

44. He must have arrived at Bologna sometime in October. See Allen, *Ep. Eras.* I, Ep. 200, pp. 431-32.

45. *Ibid.,* I, Ep. 205, p. 435. In *ibid.,* I, Ep. 200, p. 432 he had expressed his hope that he might return to Bologna once the Bentivogli tyrants had fled and peace had been restored. In Ep. 203, *ibid.,* I, p. 433, dated from Bologna, November 16, 1506, Erasmus notes Julius' entrance into the city and that on the following day he celebrated mass. There is more than a slight suggestion of contrast here between priest and conqueror. That he actually saw this triumphal entry of Julius II —as well as his later entry into Rome—is attested by a statement some years later in his notes to the New Testament which contains provoca-

tive parallels to both phrases and sentiments in the *Julius exclusus*. See *Erasmi Opera Omnia . . .* ed. LeClerc (Luduni Batavorum: Petrus Vander Aa, 1704), VI, 455 F, hereafter cited as Erasmus, *Opera Omnia*. In *ibid.*, IX, 361 B, we find Erasmus again referring to having seen these two "triumphs" of Julius in Bologna and Rome. The passage immediately following also suggests the phrasing of the *Julius exclusus*, ll. 1078-79. Nolhac, *op. cit.*, p. 26, contends that the shock of seeing the Vicar of Christ in such warlike occupation was never effaced from Erasmus' memory.

46. He probably went to Venice in the early spring of 1508 and left in the early winter of the same year. See Allen, *Ep. Eras.*, I, Ep. 207, pp. 437-39; Ep. 209, pp. 440-42; Ep. 210, p. 443; Ep. 211, pp. 443-47; and Ep. 212, pp. 447-48. See also the detailed section on the Aldine edition of the *Adagia* in Margaret M. Phillips, *The 'Adages' of Erasmus*, pp. 62-95.

47. The stay in Padua is documented by only two letters, both dated in December, 1508. See *ibid.*, I, Epp. 212-13, pp. 447-49, and Ep. 215, p. 450.

48. Cf. *Julius exclusus*, n. 34.

49. Apparently Erasmus was in and out of Rome several times but the chronology is very difficult. Allen puts him in Rome at the end of February 1509, in April, and at the beginning of July. See *Ep. Eras.*, I, Ep. 216, intro. p. 452.

50. See *ibid.*, I, Ep. 296, p. 568, and II, Epp. 333-34, intro. pp. 69, 73, and Ep. 335, pp. 79-90, to Leo X.

51. In the *Ciceronianus*, Erasmus, *Opera Omnia*, I, 993 A, in discussing a declamation held at the court of Julius, clearly indicates that he was there for, he says, "I do not refer to rumor but to what I heard with my own ears and saw with my own eyes."

52. Allen, *Ep. Eras.*, I, "Catalogus Lucubrationum," p. 37. He further states that the originals were lost, as were evidently the copies he later made of them. In the "Dulce bellum inexpertis," he refers to this matter again and to a "book entitled *Antipolemus*, which I wrote when living in Rome, for Pope Julius II, at the time when he was deliberating whether to make war on Venice," Margaret M. Phillips, *The 'Adages' of Erasmus*, p. 348. See also Erasmus, *Opera Omnia*, II, 968 C.

53. Allen, *Ep. Eras.*, I, Epp. 214-15, pp. 449-52.

54. The inception of this book was described by Erasmus in the

letter of dedication he addressed to More, *ibid.*, I, Ep. 222, p. 460. He mentions it again in the "Catalogus Lucubrationum," *ibid.*, I, p. 19, as well as in *ibid.*, II, Ep. 337, p. 94 to Martin van Dorp.

55. The edition used is that of Leonard F. Dean, *The Praise of Folly* by Desiderius Erasmus, a New Translation, with Introduction and Notes (New York: Farrar, Straus, 1946), p. 111.

56. *Ibid.*, p. 112.

57. *Ibid.*, pp. 112-13.

58. For all his claim of having "dashed off" *The Praise of Folly* in a matter of days, it was not published until the summer of 1511, and must have taken some work to be put in its final form. See Allen, *Ep. Eras.*, I, Ep. 222, intro. pp. 459-60. He may already have been doing some work toward his New Testament and his edition of St. Jerome. The next few years were to be crowded with work, some of which must already have been in one stage or another. See *ibid.*, I., Ep. 296, p. 570, II, Ep. 373, pp. 164-66, intro. note, as well as P. S. Allen, "Erasmus' Services to Learning," *British Academy Proceedings, 1924-25*, XI (1927), 358. See Allen, *Ep. Eras.*, I, "Catalogus Lucubrationum," pp. 6, 8, 9, and 21; *ibid.*, I, Ep. 175, p. 388, n.; and C. Reedijk (ed.), *The Poems of Desiderius Erasmus* (Leiden: E. J. Brill, 1956), intro. Carmen 85, pp. 291-92 and intro. Carmen 47, p. 255.

59. His customary poverty made this difficult. He stayed with several of his scholar friends, notably More and Grocin and possibly Colet. See *ibid.*, II, Ep. 337, p. 94 and "Catalogus Lucubrationum," I, p. 19; Ep. 241, pp. 484-85; Ep. 237, p. 478; Ep. 227, p. 467; and Ep. 230, p. 471. For a time he shared a lodging with Ammonio. See *ibid.*, I, Ep. 221, pp. 458-59.

60. This in a letter to Servatius at the end of 1505; *ibid.*, I, Ep. 185, p. 415.

61. Fisher had offered this position to Erasmus and the latter had accepted when his opportunity to go to Italy had cancelled the arrangements. See *ibid.*, I, Ep. 225, p. 465, n. and Appendix VI, pp. 590-93.

62. The standard Latin text is in Ferguson, *Opuscula*, pp. 35-37.

63. Pineau, *op. cit.*, 385-415, makes a careful collation of the epigram and the *Julius exclusus* demonstrating a striking parallelism of phrase and sentiment. Ferguson draws the same conclusion in his notes to the epigram and to the *Julius*. See *Opuscula*, pp. 35-36 and

pp. 65-124, passim. The affinities of reference, phrasing, and even of grammatical structure are so clear as to "cinch" the question of authorship.

64. In the standard Erasmus bibliography, Ferdinand van der Haeghen, *Bibliotheca Erasmiana: Répertoire des Oeuvres d'Érasme* (Ghent: Bibliothéque de l'Université, 1893), the epigram is not included even among the works attributed to Erasmus, although the *Julius* is. See Pineau, *op. cit.*, 385-415 and especially 385-87 for his text of the epigram with elaborate notes and comments on the striking resemblance between the epigram and the *Julius*.

65. Ferguson, *Opuscula*, p. 35.

66. Cornelis Reedijk, "Een Schimpdicht van Erasmus op Julius II," *Opstellen door Vrienden en Collegas aangeboden aan Dr. F. K. H. Kossmann* (The Hague: Nijhoff, 1958), pp. 186-207, concludes that "the poem is without doubt done by Erasmus." He even holds that the hastily written words on the back of the manuscript are also in Erasmus' hand.

67. Allen, *Ep. Eras.*, I, Ep. 233, pp. 472-73.

68. *Ibid.*, I, Ep. 227, pp. 267-68.

69. Translation from Nichols, *Letters,* Ep. 275, pp. 102-3. Cf. Allen, *Ep. Eras.*, I, Ep. 282, pp. 541-42.

70. *Ibid.*, I, Ep. 282, pp. 541-42 and the letters dated from London, Ep. 252, pp. 498-99; Ep. 253, pp. 499-500; Ep. 254, pp. 500-501; Ep. 260, pp. 510-12; Ep. 261, pp. 512-13; Epp. 264-69, pp. 517-25.

71. *Ibid.*, I, Ep. 228, p. 468.

72. *Ibid.* I, Ep. 232, p. 472.

73. *Ibid.*, I, Ep. 233, p. 473.

74. *Ibid.*, I, Ep. 218, Allen's biographical note, p. 455; and II, Ep. 521, p. 442, intro. See the fuller discussion of this point in Clemente Pizzi, *Un Amico di Erasmo L'Umanista Andrea Ammonio* (Florence: Felice Le Monnier, 1956), pp. 16-18.

75. In a letter to Erasmus dated November 18 [1511] Ammonio, in decrying his own misfortunes, cites the example of two Italian friends who had succeeded, the one in becoming "Romanae ecclesiae Vicecancellarium" and the other "summum Poenitentiarium." Allen, *Ep. Eras.*, I, Ep. 243, p. 487, n. identifies them as Sisto della Rovere of Lucca, nephew of Julius II, and Lionardo Grosso della Rovere, nephew of Sixtus IV, and thus connects Ammonio not only with the inner circle of Roman officialdom but, significantly for this study, with the

family of Julius II. See also Pizzi, *op. cit.,* pp. 15-18, 24; and Pizzi's edition of Andreae Ammonii *Carmina Omnia* (Florence: Olschki, 1958), Appendix I, pp. 71-72, which also suggests Ammonio's connection with the Julian circle.

76. Allen, *Ep. Eras.,* I, Ep. 218, intro. p. 455. By mid-summer 1511 he had entered royal service as Latin Secretary to Henry VIII.

77. Allen, *Ep. Eras.,* I, Ep. 236, p. 476.

78. *Ibid.,* I, Ep. 239, p. 481.

79. *Ibid.,* I, Ep. 245, p. 492.

80. *Ibid.,* I, Ep. 247, p. 494.

81. *Ibid.,* I, Ep. 251, p. 498.

82. Of this letter all that remains is a two line abstract and the phrase which is here quoted, *ibid.,* I, Ep. 257, p. 508.

83. Erasmus mentions this business in *ibid.,* I, Ep. 252, p. 498; Ep. 253, p. 500; and Ep. 255, pp. 501-2. The commission of Fisher is cited in J. S. Brewer (ed.), *Letters and Papers, Foreign and Domestic, of the Reign of Henry VIII* (Great Britain: Public Record Office, 1863), I, 2085. The pope's motives in delaying the council are explained by the complex fortunes of war and diplomacy but there seems no objective evidence for attributing worse motives to him. Erasmus, however, makes the pope in the dialogue the cynical manipulator of the council. See ll.570-88 and n. 74.

84. Allen, *Ep. Eras.,* I, Ep. 262, p. 513.

85. For the prefatory letter see *ibid.,* I, Ep. 164, pp. 373-75, and intro. note; for the account of its inception, *ibid.,* I, pp. 19-20; and the extended preface to the Froben edition of 1518, *ibid.,* III, Ep. 858, pp. 361-77.

86. Allen, *Ep. Eras.,* I, Ep. 182, pp. 407-12, the preface to the *Adnotationes,* and n. See *ibid.,* II, Ep. 384, p. 182, n. for a suggestion of the connection between the Valla work and his own edition of the New Testament.

87. This point is asserted strongly by Nolhac, *op. cit.,* p. 63. See also Johan Huizinga, *Erasmus and the Age of Reformation* (New York: Harper and Bros., 1957), p. 67; Phillips, *Erasmus and the Northern Renaissance,* pp. 61-63; and *The 'Adages' of Erasmus,* pp. 101-2.

88. In Allen, *Ep. Eras.,* I. Ep. 246, p. 493, he may allude to new work on Lucian's *Icaromenippus.* The same may be the case with some of Seneca's tragedies, *ibid.,* I, p. 13, and Ep. 264, p. 517, which mention not only certain works of Lucian and Seneca but "complusculos

Plutarchi libros, quos emendatos addemus." There is another reference to work on Plutarch in *ibid.,* I, Ep. 271, p. 528 and Ep. 272, pp. 529-30.

89. He prepared for Colet's school at this time the *De Copia,* translated and emended Lily's *De Syntaxi,* and wrote some devotional poems. See the description in the "Catalogus Lucubrationum," *ibid.,* I, pp. 6, 8, 9 and 21 and the prefatory epistles in *ibid.,* I, Ep. 260, pp. 510-12; Ep. 175, pp. 388-89.

90. See J. J. Mangan, *The Life, Character, and Influence of Desiderius Erasmus of Rotterdam* (New York: The Macmillan Co., 1927), I, 327, and Allen's notes in *Ep. Eras.,* II, to Epp. 373 and 384, pp. 164-72, 181-84.

91. The concept behind the term "Philosophia Christi" had long been a prominent part of Erasmus' own philosophy but it becomes the thesis of the important little *Praefatio* which, along with several other pieces, served as introduction to the first edition of the *Novum Instrumentum* called ". . . Paraclesis, id est, adhortatio, ad Christianae Philosophiae Studium." See Erasmus, *Opera Omnia,* VI, preface, unnumbered pp.

92. See, for example, the group of his earliest letters, Allen, *Ep. Eras.,* I, Epp. 11-16, pp. 85-91, as well as the discussion of these letters in *ibid.,* I, Appendix III, p. 585. See also *ibid.,* I, Epp. 19-20, pp. 95 ff, as well as some of the Parisian letters, for example, *ibid.,* I, Ep. 64, p. 192; Ep. 58, especially the intro., pp. 174 ff; Ep. 55, pp. 169 ff; and Ep. 56, pp. 171 ff. Particularly important in this connection is his first major work which may be called humanistic, the *Antibarbarorum Liber,* written shortly before leaving Steyn. The best text is that reproduced in Albert Hyma, *op. cit.,* Appendix B, see especially pp. 253, 256, 259, 268-69, 271, 273, 279, 281, and 282 ff.

93. Renaudet, *op. cit.,* pp. 86-87, remarks the penetrating wisdom and singular freedom of expression with which Erasmus attacked the political "system" in the commentaries on the adages "Aut regem aut fatuum," "Festina lente," and "Spartam nactus es." Yet probably the most famous of the Erasmian adages, the "Dulce bellum inexpertis," appeared only with the Froben edition of 1515, growing out of a letter to Anthony of Bergen, Allen, *Ep. Eras.,* I, Ep. 288, pp. 551-54.

94. See Ferguson, *Opuscula,* pp. 32 ff., 53; E. Rodocanachi, *Histoire de Rome. Le Pontificat de Jules II (1503-1513),* p. 103; and Margaret M. Phillips, *The 'Adages' of Erasmus,* pp. 101-2.

95. Ferguson, *Opuscula,* p. 53. The letter is also cited in Roger

Aubenas and Robert Ricard, *L'Eglise et la Renaissance (1449-1517)*, vol. XV of *Histoire de l'Eglise depuis les origines jusqu'à nos jours* (N.P.: Bloud and Gay, 1951), p. 161.

96. See n. 14 and n. 15 above.

97. Aubenas and Ricard, *op. cit.,* p. 161 and Renaudet, *Érasme et l'Italie,* p. 106, and Renaudet, *Préréforme et Humanisme à Paris,* pp. 200 ff.

98. Cf. *Julius exclusus,* l. 587.

99. Renaudet, *Préréforme et Humanisme à Paris,* pp. 544-46.

100. Aubenas and Ricard, *op. cit.,* p. 161.

101. *Ibid.,* p. 162. These "gravures satiriques," as well as other anti-papal efforts encouraged by Louis XII, are also discussed in Pastor, *op. cit.,* VI, 357-60.

102. See the work, *Le traicté de la différence des schismes et des conciles de l'église, et de la préeminence et utilité des Conciles de la Sainte Eglise Gallicane,* in *Oeuvres* de Jean Lemaire de Belges, ed. J. Stecher, Vol. III *Oeuvres Diverses* (Louvain: Imprimerie Lefever, 1885), pp. 231-359, especially pp. 317-18. See also Aubenas and Ricard, *op. cit.,* p. 161; Emile Foquet, *A Literary History of France* (New York: Scribner's Sons, 1907), p. 206; G. Lanson and Paul Tuffrau, *Histoire de la Littérature Française* (Paris: Librairie Hachette, 1951), p. 186; and especially Paul Spaak, *Jean Lemaire de Belges, sa vie, son oeuvre et ses meilleures pages* (Paris: Librairie Champion, 1926), pp. 83-84.

103. Charles Oulment in his *Pierre Gringore* (Paris: Librairie spécial pour l'histoire de France, 1911), pp. 32-46, traces the development of this propaganda through the work of Gringore, the most important of the court dramatists. Nikolaus Hamper, *Die Stellung des Dichters Pierre Gringore zur französischen Kirchenpolitik unter Ludwig XII* (Metz: Druckerie der Lothringen Zeitung, 1912), p. 32, makes the case that he was the instrument of the centralizing monarchy in Louis' fight with the papacy. See also *ibid.,* pp. 17-18, as well as Renaudet, *Erasme et l'Italie,* p. 106.

104. *Oeuvres complètes* de [Pierre] Gringore, ed. Ch. d'Hericault and A. de Montaiglon (Paris: P. Jannet, 1858), I, 169-83. This work is also characterized rather fully in Renaudet, *Préréforme et Humanisme à Paris,* p. 531, where he suggests a possible relationship with the theme of the *Julius.* See also his *Érasme et l'Italie,* p. 106.

105. Gringore, *op. cit.,* I, 157-67. See also Aubenas and Ricard, *op. cit.,* pp. 161-62 and Oulment, *op. cit.,* p. 37.

106. Gringore, *op. cit.*, I, 198-286, especially the third division of the play called "Moralité." For a detailed analysis see Oulment, *op. cit.*, pp. 271 ff.; and E. Picot, "Les Moralités polemiques ou la Controverse religieuse dans l'ancien Théâtre français, T. Moralité par Pierre Gringore," *Bulletin Société de l'Histoire du Protestantisme français. Etudes historiques*, pp. 225-32.

107. See n. 10 above.

108. The resemblance between the Julius dialogue and these several French court pieces and popular jests actually ends with the criticism of contemporary affairs and the retailing of current gossip about the pope; it is, moreover, a resemblance shared with dozens of other pieces. Erasmus may certainly have absorbed some impression from them but he was not familiar enough with vernacular forms nor was he sympathetic enough to them to have made any extensive borrowing. See Oulment, *op. cit.*, pp. 67 ff; Spaak, *op. cit.*, p. 84; and Renaudet, *Erasme et l'Italie*, pp. 104-6.

109. Allen, *Ep. Eras.*, I, Ep. 130, p. 304, n. 92 and Ep. 56, p. 171, intro. See also P. Smith, *op. cit.*, pp. 2-5. They were not published, however, until 1518-19 by Froben. See the early editions in van der Haeghen, *op. cit.*

110. Erasmus, *Opera Omnia*, I, 186-340; and Allen, *Ep. Eras.*, I, p. 18; Ep. 187, pp. 416-17; Ep. 205, p. 435; and Ep. 246, p. 493. See also Craig R. Thompson, *The Translations of Lucian by Erasmus and St. Thomas More* (Ithaca: Vail-Ballou Press, 1940) and Renaudet, *Erasme et l'Italie*, p. 96.

111. Margaret M. Phillips, *The 'Adages' of Erasmus*, p. 96 ff.

112. There are over 400 references to Plato in the *Adagia*, almost 600 to Aristophanes, 475 to Horace, 99 to Persius, 92 to Martial, 127 to Juvenal, and 335 to Lucian. See *ibid.*, Appendix III, pp. 393-403.

113. Walter Kaiser, *Praisers of Folly: Erasmus, Rabelais, Shakespeare* (Cambridge: Harvard University Press, 1963), p. 37.

114. *Ibid.*, p. 24.

115. *Ibid.*, p. 61. See also Alvin Kernan, *The Cankered Muse: Satire of the English Renaissance* (New Haven: Yale University Press, 1959), pp. 28-29.

116. *The Anatomy of Satire* (Princeton: Princeton University Press, 1962), p. 18.

Notes on the Text

1. See Matt. 16:19 for the scriptural basis of the famous papal claim to the "power of the keys." It seems apparent that the author is drawing the none too subtle inference that Julius, in not having the "right key," is not and has never been legitimately pope, in the sense of possessing the higher spiritual power that the keys symbolize and that should have descended through the papal office from Peter. The business of the keys may merely be connected with the militant reputation of the pope as reflected in the jokes and jibes of the Roman wags who claimed that Julius had thrown St. Peter's keys into the Tiber and wouldn't know the sword of St. Paul. They no longer called him *claviger* (the key bearer) but *armiger* (the arms bearer). See E. Rodocanachi, *Histoire de Rome. Le Pontificat de Jules II (1503-1513)* (Paris: Librairie Hachette, 1928), p. 103. There is an interesting passage in the adage "Scarabeus aquilam quaerit," which may well be an echo of this exchange, in which Erasmus refers to "some of the Roman Pontiffs—they who may go straight to heaven because they have the keys," Margaret M. Phillips, *The 'Adages' of Erasmus,* p. 249.

2. The crest of the Rovere family featured a golden oak tree probably from the Latin *robur,* "oak" and Roboreus = Rovere. Oaks and acorns frequently figured in the decoration of Julius' monuments as, for example, the ropes of oak leaves and acorns borne by some of the nude youths in Michelangelo's Sistine ceiling murals. See Charles de Tolnay, *Michelangelo,* Vol. II., *The Sistine Ceiling* (Princeton: Princeton University Press, 1945), p. 162. Julius and his uncle, the former Pope Sixtus IV, both belonged apparently to a non-noble or less noble branch of the family. The noble branch used the golden oak

device while the other's was natural. Sixtus, however, had appropriated the more exalted crest, claiming that his high office merited his "converting our tree to gold." Leonce de Villeneuve, *Recherches sur la Famille della Rovere: Contribution pour servir à l'histoire du Pape Jules II* (Rome: A. Befani, 1887), p. 12.

3. Julius was as great a patron of the minor arts as of painting, sculpture, and architecture. In this regard he had made for him many new vestments, table service, and at least one tiara valued at 200,000 ducats and made by the jeweler Ambrogio Foppa, known as Caradosso, of Milan: see Rodocanachi, *op. cit.,* p. 82. Erasmus may well have seen these things in Rome and carried away his impression of "conspicuous consumption." He may have "borrowed" the reference at first or second hand, for there is an interesting parallel in the anti-papal writings of Jean Lemaire de Belges, in Spaak, *op. cit.,* p. 85, where he speaks of "present day popes" wearing a tiara tall and pointed and jewel-encrusted which would put an oriental despot to shame. Cf. l. 34 below, "barbarus unquam tyrannus." There is a passage in the adage "Sileni Alcibiadis" in which Erasmus describes the same sort of "exterior," glittering with jewels and gold from head to foot, "but open the Silenus, and you find nothing but a soldier, a trader, or finally a despot," Margaret M. Phillips, *The 'Adages' of Erasmus,* p. 277.

4. The precise distinction between the two symbolic keys that is made here is somewhat obscure. Perhaps it is the distinction suggested in Louis Reau, *Iconographie de l'art Chrétien* (Paris: Les Presses universitaires de France, 1955), III, 1083, where he observes that Peter is usually shown with two keys, one silver and the other gold, and that they signify the key to heaven and the key to earth; the power to bind and the power to loose, given by Christ to the chief of the Apostles; and, together, the power to open and close. The reference might also be to the medieval distinction between the key to power and the key to knowledge. Cf. Luke 11:52.

5. Acts 8:18-24. The dialogue returns frequently to the charge of simony against Julius.

6. Julius' family came from this section of the Piedmont and drew strong support from there. This was, for example, one of Julius' principal refuges during the perilous years of Alexander VI's pontificate. See Villeneuve, *op. cit.,* pp. 23 ff., 67.

7. Mercury Trismegistus was a kind of "bastard," composite deity

of Egyptian-Greek origin. The term is simply a translation of an Egyptian title, "Thoth, the Very-Great." Erasmus here apparently means it to stand simply for greatness. He is probably also playing with the ancient classical formula "Jupiter Optimus Maximus," and implying that the "Pontifex Maximus" must also be "Pontifex Optimus."

8. The whole foregoing passage depends upon the double meaning of the word "sanctus," both "saint" and "holy." Cf. the formula of papal address, "Your Holiness."

9. The first reference to Julius' drunkenness, which will be elaborated in the course of the dialogue. Cf. ll. 84-85 and the Julian epigram, introduction pp. 18-19. This is part of the flood of anti-papal propaganda which Erasmus so freely exploited. Pastor, *op. cit.*, VI, 223, n. denies the charge, saying, "That he was addicted to drink is an invention of his political enemies." Rodocanachi, *op. cit.*, p. 81 calls the charge "a calumny" and in n. 4, pp. 81-82, indicates two hostile Venetian sources for it. Francesco Guicciardini, *The History of Italy,* tr. A. P. Goddard (London: Z. Stuart, 1763), IV, 28-29 alludes to references to "the Pope's immoderate Love of Wine," as if it were a matter of common knowledge.

10. This ironic reference to Julius' "holy mind" can be referred directly to the same allusion in the "Julius Epigram," introduction, p. 19, above; and, of course, to the classical references to Caesar's "falling sickness." See Plutarch, *Caesar,* A. H. Clough (ed.), IV, 105, 145; and Suetonius, *Caesar,* Modern Library Edition, p. 27.

11. The papal armies were, in fact, no worse than the others that ravaged Italy in these years. They were all comprised largely of mercenaries who presented much the appearance that Erasmus describes here.

12. This word portrait of Julius, while allowing the satirist his latitude for exaggeration, is not altogether out of line with other contemporary descriptions of the "terrible pope." See Pastor, *op. cit.,* VI, 212-14 on the pope's "going in arms."

13. Again the comparison which recurs in the dialogue and which is the chief theme of the Julian epigram.

14. Julius' reputation for physical violence was part of his "image." In his life of Michelangelo, Giorgio Vasari, *Lives of the Most Eminent Painters, Sculptors, & Architects,* tr. and ed. Mrs. J. Foster (London: G. Bell & Sons, 1878), VI, 252 tells of an incident: when Michel-

angelo finally returned to the pope's service and came to him in Bologna, one of the attending bishops made a disparaging remark about the artist and "this threw the Pope into such a rage that he fell upon the Bishop with a stick which he had in his hand, exclaiming, "tis thou that art the ignoramus, with the impertinencies thou art pouring forth, and which are such as we should ourselves not think of uttering'; he then caused the Bishop to be driven out by the usher in waiting, with blows of his fist." Vasari, *ibid.,* V. 266-67 recounts another incident when the pope in a rage struck Michelangelo with his staff. Guicciardini, *op. cit.,* V, 94 tells of an envoy who advocated a course of action which displeased Julius, whereupon the pope "ordered him to be immediately clapt into Prison, and examined on the Rack"—presumably as a spy! Rodocanachi, *op. cit.,* p. 7 records another instance of Julius' attacking a man with his stick. And M.A.J. Dumesnil, *Histoire de Jules II, sa Vie et son Pontificat* (Paris: Librairie Renouard, 1873), p. 232 tells how he threatened to have the poet Ariosto thrown into the sea when he dared appear before him as the emissary of Alfonso d'Este.

15. Here is meant apparently the power to celebrate the mass.

16. This is a sly and ironic extension of the strict rules governing papal elections to which Julius himself contributed substantially by his Bull, *Cum tam divino,* directed against simoniacal elections. Strictly speaking the point involved here is not covered by the regulations but, given the general notion of the unbroken continuity of papal authority, Julius has a point of sorts.

17. Erasmus refers to this again in the *Adagia,* Erasmus, *Opera Omnia,* II, 823 A, item LXXXVI, using it to illustrate the maxim, "a remo ad tribunal," saying further, "it is rumored" that Julius as a young man performed this sort of menial sailor's work. The source of this rumor, while not precisely known, was undoubtedly part of the anti-papal propaganda which Julius' activities so abundantly encouraged. Moritz Brosch, *Papst Julius II, und die Gründung des Kirchenstaates* (Gotha: Friedrich Andreas Perthes, 1878), p. 301, n. 5 notes the widespread contemporary references to Julius' low birth, including a statement made by Louis XII to a Florentine ambassador: "The pope is a peasant who must be driven with a stick." See also *ibid.,* pp. 1, 3-4. Villeneuve, *op. cit.,* pp. 12-13, and n. cites two highly suspect French and Venetian sources on the family of Julius and his uncle and remarks of the latter, ". . . he was born of

common stock. His father was a fisherman." He goes on to suggest, *ibid.,* pp. 23 ff, however, that the family records, though they are sketchy, indicate a leading position in Liguria as early as the early fifteenth century.

18. Julius was indeed the nephew of Pope Sixtus IV, but not "by his sister," as l. 297 below claims. It was his father, Raffaelo della Rovere, who was the brother of the Francesco della Rovere who became Sixtus IV. Like his uncle, and probably through his connections, Julius joined the Franciscan Order.

19. Julius' public career began with the elevation of Sixtus IV, one of the most notorious of papal dynasts and nepotists. See Villeneuve, *op. cit.,* p. 10. The nephew was made Cardinal of San Pietro in Vincoli within a matter of months (December 15, 1471) and rapidly piled up preferments and benefices until he became one of the most powerful ecclesiastics in Europe. This, coupled with his outstanding abilities, made Julius a force to be reckoned with in church affairs for more than thirty years before his own pontificate.

20. See n. 10 above.

21. In spite of his demonic vigor Julius suffered from a series of ailments which may in part have accounted for his disposition. In discussing his strenuous activities in the fall of 1506, Rodocanachi, *op. cit.,* p. 71 and n. 3, observes that he was in ill health, suffering from rheumatism and "other" things which he quotes Paris de Grassis as identifying as "the disease the origin of which was attributed by the Italians to the French and by the French to the Neapolitans."

22. After following his uncle into the Franciscan Order, he became Prior of the Abbey of Pont-Saint-Esprit. He prospered during the pontificate of his uncle and even under Sixtus' successor, Innocent VIII. The following is a list of his principal ecclesiastical positions: 1471, Bishop of Carpentras and Cardinal of San Pietro in Vincoli; 1472, Bishop of Lausanne; 1473, Bishop of Catana; 1474, Bishop of Messina; 1475, Bishop of Avignon: 1476, Bishop of Coutances; 1477, Bishop of Viviers; 1478, Bishop of Mende; 1479, Bishop of Sabine; 1483, Bishop of Ostia and of Bologna; 1488, Administrator of Lodeve; 1499, Bishop of Savona; 1502, Bishop of Verceil. He was, moreover, three times on diplomatic missions to France and was papal legate over a number of regions. See the detailed account in Rodocanachi, *op. cit.,* p. 3, n. 1. For the troubles which paralleled this sequence of preferments, especially those following the accession of

his enemy Alexander VI, see Brosch, *op. cit.,* pp. 27-29, 34 ff. and 50 ff. See also the passage in Dumesnil, *op. cit.,* p. 31 which so remarkably echoes Julius' claims here.

23. Matt. 26:69-75; Mark 14:67-72; Luke 22:56-62; John 18:17.

24. While this was undoubtedly one of the current hostile rumors about Julius, who is charged at several other places in this dialogue with "sorcery," I can find no specific source for the reference.

25. Julius had long had important and influential connections with France. As early as 1476 he was sent as Papal Legate there. In the next few years he was successful in a number of delicate negotiations with the French court and was so closely identified with French interests that it was a detriment to his candidacy for the papal office in 1492. The vote went instead, and over his strenuous opposition, to his enemy Rodrigo Borgia, who became Alexander VI. It was at this point that Julius became "an exile." He did have to flee Rome but he found a ready refuge in France, where he was instrumental in inducing the foolish young Charles VIII to invade Italy, hoping to seize the papacy when Alexander was deposed. This, of course, did not happen and Julius returned to his French "exile" until Alexander's death in 1503. Then he returned to take an active part in the conclave which elected the short-lived Pius III. With Pius' death—less than a month after his election and ten days after his coronation—Julius finally reached the papacy. He did so not so much "through the aid of the French" as by taking advantage of the political struggle between French and Spanish interests in the College of Cardinals. The issues were clear at the time of the earlier conclave which elected Pius III. The French party had pushed the candidacy of the powerful Cardinal d'Ambroise. The Spanish cardinals were divided. And Julius, while he was unable to swing enough Italian cardinals to his own candidacy, was still able to keep d'Ambroise from the papacy. A compromise was reached in the aged Cardinal Francesco Piccolomini, who became Pius III. Julius continued to court his colleagues. He managed to consolidate the Italian faction and win enough support from the Spanish cardinals that, upon the death of Pius III, he was elected on November 1, 1503, in the shortest conclave on record: it was over before the doors of the chamber could be closed. The French certainly did not give their "aid" to Julius: they were rather the victims of his shrewd political tactics.

26. The great Catholic ecclesiastical historian Ludwig von Pastor is worth quoting at length on the financial scandal of Julius' election,

op. cit., VI, 209, n.: "Sägmüller, 133, says it seems probable that the election of Julius II was simoniacal; I should say rather it was certain. The Ferrarese Envoy Costabili, in his Despatch of 1st Nov., 1503 (State Archives, Modena, French translation in Petrucelli, I, 464), makes this more clear than A. Giustinian and Machiavelli, as he furnishes the exact amounts of the bribes given to the different electors. *Cf.* also the Despatch of Costabili of 30th Oct., cited *supra.* There is no doubt that what Priuli says of the bribery of the Spanish Cardinals is true. See Gregorovius, VIII, 17, ed. 3, also *supra.* But the report of Cardinal Adriano da Corneto to Henry VII, 4th Jan., 1504 (Gairdner, II, 112), which says that very few of the electors were quite unimpeachable in the matter, is more universally received. Of the innumerable promises made by Julius, Costabili writes in a Despatch (partly in cypher) of 8th Nov., 1503 (Rohano), *poi me subiunse formaliter credo che S.Sta.* (in cypher) *habi promesso tanto in questa sua electione* (cypher) *che haria da fare asai ad observalo.* State Archives, Modena."

27. The stock character of the braggart soldier in the *Eunuchus* of Terence.

28. ". . . when a benefice fell vacant the pope would grant it only to a prelate already holding an office which he would then have to give up, making money for the pope," Rodocanachi, *op. cit.,* p. 34. Brosch, *op. cit.,* p. 274 confirms this and notes the unprecedented scale of Julius' sale of offices and benefices.

29. Julius found the papal currency so corrupted that he had to institute far-reaching monetary reforms to correct the disparity between nominal values and the purchasing power of coins. In the process he introduced the new silver coins known as Giuli. This sort of reform resulted in considerably improved economic conditions from which the pope doubtless realized some revenues. But the implication here that the "new currency" represented some sort of unsavory manipulation is distinctly false.

30. Cf. Erasmus' *Adagia, Opera Omnia,* II, 70 B, item IV. The reference is to Cicero, *Tusc. Disput.* IV and Lucian, *Philopseudes,* and signifies the use of one evil to drive out another.

31. Julius grew a long, white beard in the course of his illness in Bologna in the fall and winter of 1510. It was a clear break with papal custom and caused widespread speculation. Some considered it the result of a vow, others thought it was done in spite, in chagrin, or in

disappointment. From whatever motive, it tended to set something of a bearded style for his successors, among them Clement VII, Paul III, and Julius III. Julius is depicted with the beard in Raphael's famous portrait.

32. While it is true that the battle of Ravenna was a bloody slaughter, the news from the battlefield was surely not "golden" to Julius for, in spite of the slaughter, it was a decisive French victory. In the long run, however, it was turned to the advantage of the pope, less by his efforts than by the general fear of French preponderance in Italy. The immediate effect of the battle of Ravenna was to weaken the pope's alliances, but a reaction set in almost at once. The Emperor Maximilian, the English king, and the Swiss all feared the menace of France and drew close to Julius' league, with substantial military support. Thus, in spite of their victory at Ravenna, the French found themselves in an untenable position, threatened by several field armies and France herself threatened with invasion, and were forced to withdraw from Italy: the victory at Ravenna became, therefore, the turning point in Louis XII's Italian campaign.

33. In the summer of 1511 Julius became seriously ill and was reported dead. Erasmus even heard rumors of it in England. See introduction, n. 71. Guicciardini, *op. cit.*, V, 268-70 notes it, and it is reported in detail in *Le due Spedizioni militari di Guilio II. tratte dal Diario di Paride Grassi Bolognese Maestro delle Cerimonie della Capella Papale* . . . con documenti e note di Luigi Frati (Bologna: Regia Tipografia, 1886), pp. 294-96.

34. While it can be argued, as here, that Julius was responsible for forming and breaking the League of Cambrai, he was not wholly responsible and the league was actually initiated against his wishes. Julius had maneuvered the Emperor Maximilian into alliance with France for the purpose of attacking Venice. But, at the last moment, the French reversed themselves; Maximilian was badly beaten; and both he and the pope were furious. It was Maximilian, however, who made the first moves toward the formation of a league composed of the enemies of Venice. In late November 1508, Maximilian's confidential counsellor, Matthaeus Lang, met with representatives of Spain and England, and with the emperor's daughter Margaret, the Hapsburg regent for the Low Countries, at Cambrai. It was probably the wise and diplomatic Margaret who made the meeting both a reality and a success. By this time the French were eager to abandon Venice, that

state having proved once more a greater danger than an aid to the French cause in Italy: and thus the Cardinal d'Ambroise came to Cambrai to bind France to the agreement. The league was concluded early in December, 1508. Its published terms were innocuous enough —primarily a reconciliation between Maximilian and Louis XII and a crusade against the Turks. But its secret terms were much more important. By those terms the parties were bound to mutual support in forcing Venice to give up the landward territories on the borders of the Venetia and certain overseas possessions which she had taken from the contracting powers and others, including the papacy. France was to declare war on Venice April 1; the pope was to lay the ban and interdict upon the republic and to call in Maximilian as the Lieutenant of the Holy See. The rest of the powers were either to maintain neutrality or to support the attack on Venice. It must be stressed that this agreement was reached—even the portions involving the papacy—entirely without papal approval. There was no representative of the pope present at the negotiations. There was a provision of the treaty which would allow the pope to become a party to it if he wished. In fact, no matter what he wished, in self defence he would have to join: the shrewd Julius had been out-foxed. He became a member of the league only in March of the following year, virtually at the last moment. Much as Julius hated Venice, he saw that Venice was apt to become the pretext for further French aggrandizement—which was an even greater threat to Julius than the continued hostility of Venice. Once in the league Julius fulfilled his part of the thieves' bargain. He used his spiritual powers as the terms of the league proposed and put troops in the field to help himself to those lands of the church that Venice had held. He maintained his place in the league until Venice had been brought to her knees. Then, early in 1510, he defected, absolved the Venetians and entered into a treaty with them. The League of Cambrai had served his purposes: he was concerned lest it serve also the purposes of France, Spain, and the Empire. With his withdrawal and the negotiations which followed, the League of Cambrai was brought to an end.

35. This figure is a patent exaggeration, again probably circulated by Julius' political enemies. He had inherited an almost bankrupt treasury from Alexander VI and patiently worked to restore fiscal integrity to the papacy—even to the extent of seeming miserly to his associates and tyrannical to his subjects and subordinates. See Rodo-

canachi, *op. cit.,* pp. 32 ff. for an account of his tight-fisted financial administration and his several slippery practices. But, efficient as his financial machinery eventually became, his wars and diplomacy were costly. He may have had an income of a quarter million ducats per year and it is impossible to know the exact amount of his treasury at his death. But had he saved every penny of his revenues for his entire pontificate he would have had scarcely half the amount Erasmus credits him with. On the amount of the treasury at Julius' death Moritz Brosch, *op. cit.,* p. 273 cites two accounts: Alberto da Capri writes to Maximilian itemizing 213,000 ducats cash, four tiaras with precious stones, gold and silver plate to the value of 50,000 ducats; the Venetian Francesco Foscari estimates 250,000 ducats cash, jewelry and precious stones to the value of 150,000 ducats, and silver plate weighing 5000 marks. Brosch concludes that whatever the amount of the estate, it was the richest that any pope had left.

36. "A letter from Rome, 23 Aug. 1511, preserved by Marino Sanudo (xii.440), mentions this Jewish physician as changing the Pope's treatment; his skill in curing Julius on this occasion became famous. . . ." Erasmus had heard of the cure and wrote bitterly to Ammonio to the effect that, though Julius had recovered, the physician's art had not been enough to cure his madness. See Allen, *Ep. Eras.,* I, Ep. 240, p. 483 and n. 36. See also the more complete report of the pope's treatment and physicians in Rodocanachi, *op. cit.,* pp. 117, 137-39.

37. This curious interpretation, if it is based on anything, may derive from the orders that Julius gave, shortly before his death, to Giovanni Francesco della Rovere, the governor of the Castel San Angelo, to keep the papal treasury there out of the hands of any but the next "legally and catholicly" elected pope. *Ibid.,* p. 179 makes this point, citing from the records of the papal Master of Ceremonies Paris de Grassis, and contends it was no more than a routine precaution. He goes on to recount the last moments of Julius' life, how he begged those close to him to pray for him "for he had sinned greatly and had not bestirred himself for the good of the church as he should have done," and how they assured him of the remission of his sins and rushed forward to kiss his hand.

38. The charge of illegitimacy seems completely fabricated and does not even appear in the contemporary mass of personal vilification against the pope.

39. Julius' own unfortunate gift for satiric epigram sometimes tended to confirm the propagandists' image of him. For example, after the fall of Bologna and shortly before the pope left to return to Rome he came to see the portrait statue which he had commissioned Michelangelo to make for him, presumably celebrating his conquest of the city. The statue was finished in the clay model. The right hand was upraised but the left contained nothing. The sculptor inquired whether he should put a book in the left hand; whereupon Julius replied, "Put a sword into it, for of letters I know but little." See Vasari, *op. cit.,* V, 253. In spite of his reputation to the contrary, Julius was not unlearned. He had studied at the University of Perugia, which was the preferred school for the Italian Franciscans. When his uncle became a cardinal he seems to have placed his nephew under the tutelage of the humanist Nicolo Pandolfini. Thus Julius may be said to have had the typical education of a young man destined for public life in the Italy of his time. Moreover, some interest in humanistic learning carried over into his later life if his library is any reflection of his interests. It consisted of more than two hundred volumes, almost all of them Latin classics, including Livy, Cicero, Vergil, Ovid, and Caesar. It included also works by Petrarch, Boccaccio, Biondo, Manetti, and Bruno; and translations of Greek writers, among them a copy of Valla's translation of Herodotus. It contained also a bibliography of Roman inscriptions, a Ceremonial, a Bible, and a Digest. And they were almost all fine manuscript editions. See Rodocanachi, *op. cit.,* pp. 3, n. 1, 87-88. Rodocanachi also adduces Julius' relations with the University of Rome, concluding that even if Julius had small taste for letters, he was not hostile to freedom of thought and teaching, *ibid.,* p. 88.

40. See the Julian epigram where this charge is part of the comparison with Caesar. Cf. Suetonius, *Caesar,* Modern Library Edition, pp. 4, 29. These charges are carried over, like others, into the dialogue and with apparently as little basis. They certainly originated with his enemies. For example, Brosch, *op. cit.,* p. 351, n. 36, in discussing one of the contemporary Venetian diary accounts, contends that the charge of sodomy was probably interpolated. In the poisonous atmosphere of papal Rome the charge of unnatural vice was almost routine against any highly placed person. Julius, in this as in other things, tended to feed the rumors of his enemies. He was fond enough of a young and handsome guest-hostage at the papal court to arouse suspicion. See

Rodocanachi, *op. cit.,* p. 84. Moreover, his incredible indulgence with the incompetent and treacherous Cardinal Alidosi suggested the same thing. See n. 61 below.

41. As part of the build-up for his first attack on Bologna, such indulgences were used. They are cited in *ibid.,* p. 71, n. 1 from the Bull of Indulgence, "le texte integral" of which is reproduced in Paris de Grassis, *op. cit.,* p. 177.

42. Matt. 25:34-36.

43. Matt. 7:21-23.

44. While "the doctrine of the two swords" is based upon a scriptural passage, Luke 22:28, it was entirely a medieval politico-ecclesiastical concept, basically Augustinian. Here Julius is made to take the extreme papal position.

45. Eph. 6:17.

46. John 18:10.

47. Matt. 16:19; John 20:22.

48. Based on Matt. 26:52-53.

49. Julius customarily added this designation to his name on coins and medallions and in inscriptions. It appears in its "classical form" in the inscription over a doorway in the Belvedere, "Julius II. Pont. Max. Ligurum VI. Patria Savonensis Sixti IIII. nepos Viam hanc struxit Pont. commoditati," the "Ligurum VI." referring to the fact that he was the sixth Ligurian pope. See Julian Klaczko, *Rome and the Renaissance* . . . (New York and London: G. P. Putnam's Sons, 1903), p. 135, n. 3.

50. Sixtus IV had indeed been general of the Franciscan Order and from this office had come to the papacy. The reference is also a glancing blow at the corruption of the mendicant orders, a favorite Erasmian target. Cf. the passage immediately following ll. 307-8. Sixtus was "an outstanding military man" too. At the beginning of his pontificate he had vigorously advocated war against the Turks with no great success. He was much more successful in involving himself in wars in Italy. He was directly implicated in the Florentine Pazzi Conspiracy and, after its failure, in a war with Florence. This led him into the labyrinth of Italian secular politics and into wars and alliances with several other Italian powers which consumed most of the energy of his reign.

51. This may have been a rumor current among Julius' enemies in Italy. Some color was doubtless added to it by the notorious character

of Sixtus IV, but there seems to be no historical basis for the charge. Indeed, Brosch, *op. cit.,* p. 4 contends that the rumor that Julius was the son of Sixtus was a confusion, intentional or otherwise, by Erasmus, of gossip about other members of his family.

52. This bull was "designed to prevent the repetition of the disgraceful practices which were resorted to at the election of Alexander VI." The Bull, dated Jan. 14, 1505, ". . . declares all simoniacal elections from henceforth null, and pronounces the severest penalties of the Church on all guilty of such practices. Further, it ordains that all intermediaries and agents, whether lay or clerical, and whatever their rank, whether Prelates, Archbishops or Bishops, or Envoys of Kings or States, who are implicated in a simoniacal election are to be deprived of their dignities, and their goods are to be confiscated. The Bull forbids all promises or engagements to be contracted by Cardinals or any other persons in connection with a Papal election and declares them null and void." (Bull V., 405 *seq.*; Raynaldus, ad. an. 1506, n. 1 *seq.* and Mansi.) The Bull was not published until October 1510, from Bologna at the beginning of the war with France. It was again approved, re-enacted, and published by the Lateran Council, Feb. 16, 1513. See Pastor, *op. cit.,* VI, 440.

53. This passage is again a propaganda distortion probably picked up by Erasmus either from his anti-papal friends in Venice or in Bologna. Rodocanachi, *op. cit.,* p. 69 refers to the "rain of injurious and satiric verses composed in Bologna, Ferrara, and Venice that fell on the pope." In fact the Bentivogli were far from being popular rulers. On the contrary, they ". . . had made the name of Bentivoglio thoroughly destested in the city by their tyranny and violence," Pastor, *op. cit.,* VI, 261. This was more true of Giovanni's sons, who were cruel and dissolute, than of the old tyrant himself. He had led the almost classic career of the Italian despot through some forty years in Bologna. The people of that city had reason to be grateful to him but, unfortunately, he had chosen to be feared—or perhaps respected —rather than to be loved. See Guicciardini, *op. cit.,* IV, 113, 159-60, and 160, n. where he cites the supporting opinion of Paolo Giovio. See also Dumesnil, *op. cit.,* pp. 70-71. What is more, the papacy and even Julius II had been close parties to the tyranny, extending recognition to the illegal rule of the Bentivogli in return for ecclesiastical taxes and the recognition of papal overlordship. The Bentivogli encroachment in these areas was finally leading to the rupture of the arrangement between Julius and Giovanni Bentivoglio.

54. In addition to the financial and administrative quarrel with the Bentivogli, Julius' decision to attack Bologna was also prompted by the fact that, as Erasmus here makes him say, "it was expedient for the plans that I had in mind." It was Julius' ambition to recover the sovereignty of the Papal States, and Bologna was the key stronghold on the north. It was strategically sound, even if diplomatically dangerous, to attack this city. He personally took direction of the campaign, a classic example of Julius' use of papal spiritual powers in conjunction with diplomacy to gain political advantages. After carefully isolating Bologna by a series of treaties or understandings with neighboring Italian powers and with Venice and France, Julius launched his "thunderbolts" of interdict against the city and excommunication against the tyrant and his family. It was an unbeatable combination, especially when enforced by the presence of the pope and virtually his entire court. Even before Julius reached the city the Bentivogli fled and a delegation of citizens humbly sought the protection of the pope and the lifting of the interdict. Resistance thus melted, Julius entered the city unopposed on November 10, 1506, and the following day celebrated his famous triumph. He reaffirmed the ancient liberties of the city, reformed the taxation, and set a papal legate over its government to be advised by a citizens' council. The most authentic details of this venture and the next against Bologna are to be found in the candid diary of the Papal Master of Ceremonies under Julius II, Paris de Grassis. As far as I know only a portion of this manuscript diary has been edited and printed, that dealing with the two attacks on Bologna, *Le due spedizioni militari di Guilio II*. See, for example, the full text of the interdict against Bologna, *ibid.*, pp. 177-186 a.

55. This is a reference to the questionable status of Bologna as an imperial free city. The claim rested upon a grant of Otto the Great in the tenth century and its confirmation by Henry V in the twelfth. There was equally good legal ground for declaring it a "papal" city. These claims had been hotly argued during the time Erasmus was in Bologna and he had probably learned them from his several friends there of Ghibelline sympathy. On the question of Julius' invasion of imperial rights in Lombardy see Guicciardini, *op. cit.*, V, 72-73.

56. Matt. 6:10.

57. In many ways the key to Julius' Italian political problems was Venice, even more than Bologna. In the confusion attending the collapse of the Borgia scheme for the papal states, Venice had moved quickly into the papal territories in the north and was the clearest

menace to the papacy among the Italian states. Almost immediately upon his accession Julius began his campaign to regain the lost territories from Venice and build safeguards against her. Complex negotiations were entered into with Maximilian, the King of the Romans, with France, and with several lesser Italian powers, but the pope's purposes were necessarily subordinated to the designs of his unstable allies. It was really only after Julius' successful attack on Bologna that his allies made any common cause: the result was the formation of the League of Cambrai, with its avowed purpose of destroying Venice. Julius was a luke-warm adherent to this league for he feared further entrenchment of foreign powers in Italy even more than he feared and hated the Venetians. Indeed, he was willing to make concessions to Venice. At this juncture the arrogant Venetians, playing the calculated risk that they could hold out until the league fell apart, rebuffed the overtures of the pope and intensified their offensive against him. They denied appeal of ecclesiastical cases to Rome, disposed of ecclesiastical benefices without papal sanction, denied benefit of clergy, and continued their political machinations in northern Italy. In answer to the angry pope's complaints the Venetian ambassador replied, "Your Holiness must grow a little stronger before he can expect much from the Republic." Furious, Julius answered, "I will never rest until you are brought down to be the poor fishermen that you once were." "And we," said the ambassador, "will make a priestling of the Holy Father unless he behaves himself," quoted from Italian state archives in Pastor, *op. cit.*, VI, 308. For Julius' provocation see also Brosch, *op. cit.*, pp. 105-6.

58. Matt. 19:27.

59. The Papal States were established by the Donation of the Frankish king Pepin in the eighth century as a secular holding of the popes, making them Italian princes and subsequently involving them in the labyrinth of Italian politics. Since the end of the exile in Avignon, it had been a more or less constant part of papal policy to regain authority over this area. With the progressive secularization of the Renaissance papacy, the Papal States had tended to become not so much the Patrimony of St. Peter as the patrimony of the several papal dynasts who had preceded Julius II, most notably Alexander VI. While apparently Julius had no dynastic designs on the Papal States, he did passionately want to be their undisputed sovereign. It was this ambition which controlled his whole policy as pope. Without a firm

hold on the Papal States he could not negotiate from a position of strength either in the affairs of Italy or those of Europe.

60. The Duke of Ferrara was Alfonso d'Este (1486-1534), of one of the oldest and proudest houses in Italy. He had indeed been pressured into a marriage with Lucretia Borgia by her father Alexander VI, in 1501, as part of Alexander's scheme to place his children in strategic political spots throughout northern Italy. The reference to Lucretia as "alteram filiam" is probably to be referred to the common gossip of the time which delightedly exaggerated the number of Alexander's bastards. There was supposed to have been at least one older daughter, Girolama. While Alfonso was by no means a "homini alioqui ignavo," Lucretia's dowry did include, in addition to a vast sum of money, a number of territorial benefices. Alfonso was a well-established, popular, and effective ruler and, in the judgment of Bayard, "a wise prince, vigilant in war, who knew almost all the seven liberal arts as well as many other practical arts such as the founding of artillery." Cited from *Le bon Chevalier* in Rodocanachi, *op. cit.,* p. 108. Julius' annoyance with Alfonso stemmed from the latter's stiff-necked independence. He had refused to join Julius in his defection from the League of Cambrai and had refused to continue the tribute payments to the papacy which had been another provision of the Borgia marriage arrangement. Julius had no love for contumacious vassals, especially when they took money from him. In 1512, when Alfonso's French allies could no longer protect him, he was constrained to capitulate to Julius, who forced his total submission and his renunciation of Ferrara. Alfonso escaped from Rome, took up his duchy again, and was saved from more condign punishment only by the death of the pope. The spectacular charges which he is here accused of making against the pope were quite possibly made. But it is equally likely that Erasmus fabricated them out of the contemporary hostile gossip about Julius. See Rodocanachi, *op. cit.,* pp. 109-11.

61. The man in question here was probably Julius' favorite nephew, Francesco Maria della Rovere, who had risen, through his uncle's preferment, to be Duke of Urbino and commander of the papal army. There is no reason to believe that Julius intended to give Ferrara to Francesco Maria. He certainly intended to join it "with my realm," but probably under the direct control of the curia, and not as a vassal state. In the matter of the murder of the Cardinal of Pavia and the marriage of Julius' daughter, Erasmus was also mistaken, or perhaps

again he intentionally distorted the picture. The Cardinal of Pavia, Francesco Alidosi, was a papal favorite who was constantly rewarded by the pope in spite of his notorious incompetence and greed. Such indulgence in the otherwise worldly and hard-headed Julius gave rise to the rumor of an unnatural relationship between Alidosi and the pope. After the capture of Bologna, the cardinal was made legate of the city and surrounding territory and promptly collided with Francesco Maria della Rovere, the military commander. Hostility between them grew in bitterness, confounded by the pope's unfailing partiality for the cardinal and by the loss of Bologna until, in a rage, Francesco Maria stabbed and killed him. In contrast to the implication in the text, Julius neither ordered nor wished this vicious murder; on the contrary, he grieved deeply over it. The whole question of Julius' relationship with Alidosi is obscured by the almost unrelieved hostility of the contemporary sources toward him. Alidosi was detested by Paolo Giovio, Guicciardini, and "all the other contemporary historians!" Cardinal Bembo, who was under some obligation to him, even called him "a man without faith or religion to whom nothing was either chaste or holy." Paris de Grassis hated him. See Klaczko, *op. cit.*, pp. 240-41. Finally, the pope's daughter Felice was married not to Francesco Maria but to one of the Roman Orsini, as part of Julius' plan to placate the ancient and troublesome families of the city nobility of Rome. See the citation to the manuscript journal of Paris de Grassis, Bibl. du Roi, MS 5164. t. ll. 350 v°, in Dumesnil, *op. cit.*, 47 and n. 1. See Brosch, *op. cit.*, p. 354 and n. 60; and Rodocanachi, *op. cit.*, p. 11 and n. 2, where it is pointed out that Donna Felice, whose mother was named Lucrezia, was undoubtedly Julius' daughter and that contemporary chroniclers, ambassadors, and letter writers called her the pope's daughter without hesitation. Moreover, there may have been two other daughters who had already died.

62. As early as the election of Pius III the cardinals had brought forward a new election charter, or capitulation. It may have been the work of a reform-oriented minority in the college to which the new pope adhered or possibly a measure to short-circuit the French threat to call a general council. At any rate it called for the summoning of a general council for the reform of the church within two years after the election and made provision for triennial councils in the future. With the death of Pius III in a matter of weeks and the election of Julius II, he was constrained to accept the same terms, spelled out very specifi-

cally. "Amongst its conditions were the prosecution of the war against the Turks, and the restoration of discipline in the Church. To this end it stipulated that a General Council should be summoned within two years, that the Pope should not make war against any of the Powers without the consent of two-thirds of the Cardinals, and that the Sacred College should be consulted on all important occasions, especially in the choice of new Cardinals. In order to secure the freedom and safety of the next Council the place of meeting was to be determined by the Pope and two-thirds of the Cardinals, and in case any hindrance to its meeting should be alleged, this must be proved to the satisfaction of a similar majority." Cited from the documents and archival records in Pastor, *op. cit.*, VI, 211, and n.

63. Although Julius certainly felt no compunction about violating the terms of his election capitulation if they interfered with his "imperial" plans, I can find no record of the specific absolution alleged here. Guicciardini, *op. cit.*, III, 270-71 does record an instance of a cardinal's binding oath being absolved by Julius.

64. Cf. Suetonius, Loeb Edition, XXX, "aliis rebus pietatem colas," attributed to Caesar by Cicero.

65. The force behind the strategy of the Council of Pisa was the dead hand of Cardinal George d'Ambroise, the chief advisor to Louis XII of France: he had died before the council assembled, in 1510, but his design is apparent. It was almost purely motivated by political considerations and the personal ambitions of all concerned, but shrewdly played upon the general European sentiment for church reform. Secular and ecclesiastical policies had long since been thoroughly confused by all the contending powers in the scramble for northern Italy. Julius II had certainly done more than his share to contribute to the confusion. His defection from the League of Cambrai and his promotion of the Holy League had been a serious blow to French hopes in Italy. Louis XII and d'Ambroise resolved to counter the threat by an attack upon the spiritual prerogatives of the pope. The logical starting point was to stir up the spirit of Gallicanism to which Julius II, ironically enough, had contributed by his concessions to d'Ambroise and Louis, given earlier to try to compensate the ambitious cardinal for his loss of the papal election. Two Gallican councils or synods had already been called, at Lyons and Tours, amid a din of anti-papal propaganda, to proclaim the rights of the French king and the French church against papal encroachment. The next

step was to call a general council to meet in Pisa on September 1, 1511. Again the leading spirit was France. The calling of the council had been preceded by some active diplomatic negotiation. The fickle Emperor Maximilian especially had been induced to abandon his long-standing hostility to France and join with Louis XII in promulgating the council. His campaign against Venice, following the League of Cambrai, had been disastrous to him, and the pope's abandonment of the league and rapprochement with Venice he chose to regard as betrayal. He furthermore had ambitions to free the German church from papal control and may have seriously entertained the notion of standing for the papacy himself. Other secular powers, universities, and representatives of the church at large were also invited. Conciliar precedents were so varied and so ambiguous that several claims to legality could be put forward for the council. The authority of the monarchs Louis XII and Maximilian was supported by provisions of the decree *Frequens* of the Council of Constance. More legal substance was added by the adherence of nine cardinals in whose names and by whose spiritual authority the council was actually called: no matter that all of them had some personal grievance against Julius and most of them had egregious personal motives. The leaders of this group were French adherents such as de Brie, Briçonnet, and Philip of Luxemburg. Some were members of the Spanish party who still carried a grudge against Julius, notably Bernardino Carvajal and Francesco Borgia. Still others were partisans or relatives of Italian houses fearful or jealous of Julius. With such men and motives the Council of Pisa prepared the grandiose schemes of the pacification of Christendom, a crusade against the Turks, and the "reform of the Church in its Head and in its members." Its unspoken purpose was to destroy the political as well as the spiritual power of the papacy and clear the way for the partition of Italy. See Pastor, *op. cit.,* I, 187 and n., 192-93; VI, 352-56; *The New Cambridge Modern History* (Cambridge: The University Press, 1957), I, 302-3. See also the detailed account of the issues and proceedings of both the Gallican synods and the Council of Pisa in Aubenas and Ricard, *op. cit.,* pp. 156-60; in Renaudet, *Préréforme et Humanisme à Paris,* pp. 524 ff, 531 ff; and in his *Le concile gallican de Pise-Milan; Documents florentins (1510-1512); Bibliothèque de l'Institut français de Florence* (Université de Grenoble; 1re serie, tome VII; Paris, 1922), pp. 187-659.

66. Cf. Erasmus' *Adagia, Opera Omnia,* II, 621 F, item XXXV; 662 F, item I; and 122 D. The Cercopes were a legendary people of ancient Lydia famed for their wickedness and cunning and associated with the Hercules myths. Morychus was a popular name for a statue of Dionysus at a temple site in Sicily. Since the statue was outside the temple rather than inside, the god was regarded as being foolishly careless of his duties. The whole thing probably had quite a different significance but it was, nonetheless, the source of the proverb that Erasmus used. The Hydra of Herculean fame traditionally inhabited the fetid Lernean swamp or lake and provided a proverbial allusion to anything filthy.

67. This statement reflects the long history of conflict between the popes and councils but may refer specifically to the Bull *Execrabilis* of Pius II in 1459-60. See Pastor, *op. cit.,* III, 100-101, and n.

68. Erasmus says, "There are some who say . . .": who these might be is not clear. The theory of the deposition of heretical popes had come into prominence and had been hotly argued during the late fourteenth and fifteenth centuries in the controversies of the Great Schism and the councils. Largely as a result of these arguments the proposition had been established on the basis of a text in Gratian, Dist. 40 c.6, ". . . he who himself must sit in judgment over all may be judged by no one *unless he be discovered strayed from the faith."* This was accepted even by the papalists and superseded the judgment of St. Thomas, *De Regimine Principum,* i, 14. See Brian Tierney, *Foundations of the Conciliar Theory* (Cambridge: The University Press, 1955), pp. 8-9 and *ibid.,* pp. 248-50 for the gloss of Huguccio on this text. This was the basis for the deposition of Benedict XIII and Gregory XII by the earlier Council of Pisa.

69. Acts 15:5-29.

70. Probably a play on the contrast of "maxime" and "minime" and on the name of Maximilian.

71. Erasmus was again mistaken on this point. Maximilian maintained his adherence to the Council of Pisa as long as it held any hope of ultimate success against the Venetians. As this hope failed with the pope's progressive discrediting of the "schismatic council" and as Maximilian saw his own support contributing not so much to the disadvantage of Venice as to the advantage of France, he became favorably disposed to Julius' suggestion of a negotiated peace and a truce with Venice. For all practical purposes, by 1512 Maximilian

had withdrawn his support from France and shortly declared himself against the council.

72. This is true of three of the cardinals in the company of the schismatics—Philip of Luxemburg, Adriano da Corneto, and Carlo del Carretto. They had been anything but enthusiastic before and when the fierce pontiff faced them they capitulated, claimed that their names had been used without their knowledge, and publicly declared "they would have nothing to do with the anti-Papal Council." Pastor, *op. cit.,* VI, 363-4, and n.

73. This version of the pope's action in calling an anti-council is distinctly hostile and distorted. Within the context of the papal-monarchial, anti-conciliar tradition the adherents to the Council of Pisa were rebels and revolutionaries and indeed, outside the French circle of influence, they were generally so regarded. There was, however, sufficient virtue in the announced purpose of the council to necessitate the pope's taking countermeasures: and nothing could more effectively counter the council, which the pope had already roundly condemned and repudiated, than an official, full-dress council called by the pope himself. This tactic was adopted by Julius who, on July 25, 1511, proclaimed the Fifth Lateran Council, and his own heartfelt desire to end heresy and schism and to reform the morals of clergy and laity alike. By this proclamation Julius cut the ground from under his rebel cardinals and their French supporters and robbed the Council of Pisa of its last shred of legality. It is easy enough to see in this Julius' political and diplomatic motives, but it does not follow that he had no sincere purpose of reform. On the contrary, he carried the Lateran Council well beyond the point where it served his political purposes and, except for his death in the early weeks of 1513, might have turned it into a genuine reforming council. See Pastor, *op. cit.,* VI, 364-65. The implication of the text, that Julius deliberately manipulated the opening date of the council and "packed" the College of Cardinals, is once more a half-truth. He did appoint eight new cardinals to replace those "schismatics" who had been stripped of their offices previously. But the date of the opening had to be moved to May 3, 1512, because hostilities in northern Italy made travel too hazardous. There was no "anticipating the date I had set," as Erasmus declares; and this whole passage seems to have been completely fabricated. The point of the passage is probably to be found in the

fact that Erasmus had hoped to go to Italy in the party of Bishop Fisher. But the delay prevented Fisher—and thus Erasmus—from going. See introduction, p. 23.

74. Even before the Lateran Council met, Julius had condemned the Council of Pisa on a dozen legitimate grounds, and continued to do so through the first several sessions of the Lateran Council. The thorough eradication of his ecclesiastical opposition was the first order of business. See Pastor, *op. cit.*, VI, 406-10; 427-28. Erasmus' playing with the term "sacrosanct" council may derive from the name of the bull (*Sacrosanctae*) dated July 18, 1511, in which Julius condemned the Council of Pisa and called his Lateran Council; text in *Magnum bullarium romanorum*, I, p. 519.

75. Although d'Ambroise died in 1510 before the Council of Pisa was summoned (see n. 62 above), he was at least the architect of the French anti-papal and Italian policies. D'Ambroise, like Wolsey in England and Lang in Germany, was a brilliant, shrewd, and dedicated administrator who had attached his considerable personal ambition to his country's fortunes. He had been one of the strongest advocates of continued French intervention in Italy. Perhaps he was motivated by a genuine conviction. Certainly he was also motivated by his own aspirations to be pope. He had carefully prepared the way in the last years of Alexander VI's reign and, in the elections of 1503, was the leader of the strong French party in the College of Cardinals. But he was out-maneuvered and defeated by Giuliano della Rovere. D'Ambroise never forgave this defeat. Julius tried mightily to conciliate him, granting him virtual dictatorial powers over the church in France. But, as we have seen, d'Ambroise simply used the sentiment of Gallicanism against the papacy. His intention was to continue the French military-political pressure in northern Italy and join with it ecclesiastical pressure to defeat and depose Julius. If this succeeded then he could replace him as pope and France would become the arbiter of Italy. The careful build-up for the Council of Pisa was part of this design. Thus, while d'Ambroise was "the head of the whole business," as Erasmus makes Julius say, he was certainly not driven by any such loftly motives as are implied here. He was an ecclesiastical politician of precisely the same stamp as Julius II and playing much the same game. Erasmus, here as elsewhere, follows the line of the French anti-papal, conciliar propaganda—much of it encouraged by

d'Ambroise himself. It was a sham and we can find little trace of genuine spirituality or disposition to reform in the Cardinal of Rouen, either in his public policy or his private life.

76. The Cardinal of Santa Croce, Cardinal Bernardino Carvajal, was another ambitious ecclesiastical politician who had had designs on the papal throne. He was the leader of the Spanish party in the College of Cardinals and, like d'Ambroise, had been out-maneuvered by Julius and forced to accept him as pope. He remained, however, a bitter enemy of Julius in spite of the fact that Julius entrusted him with important positions and apparently was impressed with his genuine abilities. As regards the Council of Pisa, Carvajal did not succeed d'Ambroise as its "head" but rather, from the very beginning, was the moving spirit in the dissension of the cardinals. The original secession of the cardinals occurred in the fall of 1510, three months after d'Ambroise's death. It was almost a year later when they affixed their names and authority to the proclamation of the council. In all this Carvajal took the lead. His motives, like those of d'Ambroise, were a compound of personal and political ambition, almost innocent of any spiritual or reforming purpose.

77. See n. 65 above.

78. Such obeisance on the part of the rebel cardinals was certainly no more than perfunctory and propagandistic, if indeed it occurred at all. Again, this may be Erasmus' invention or the influence of French propaganda.

79. As to the pious behavior and honorable motives of the conciliasts implied here, there is no shred of proof. Pastor, *op. cit.*, VI, 388 concludes that "not one of [them] possessed the support of a genuine conviction."

80. For these classical arguments see Tierney, *op. cit.;* John N. Figgis, *Studies in Political Thought from Gerson to Grotius 1414-1625* (Cambridge: The University Press, 1956), pp. 31-54; and R. W. Carlyle and A. J. Carlyle, *A History of Medieval Political Theory in the West* (Edinburgh and London: Blackwood, 1938), V, 318-373.

81. This powerfully ironic and eloquent passage, representing the most loftily conciliar, reforming program, can by no stretch of either the sources or the imagination be attributed to the conciliasts of Pisa. Ferguson, *Opuscula,* p. 99, n. 639, draws the interesting conclusion, "Whether Erasmus believed that the council intended to carry out

this program or not, the affair affords him an opportunity to outline a course of reform in harmony with his own opinions." While it is conceivable that such opinions may have been privately, even sincerely held, by individuals among the Pisan conciliasts, the council as a whole was so hopelessly burdened from the beginning with base political and personal motives that its discredit could be clearly anticipated. The pope's diplomacy had isolated both Spain and England and their monarchs refused to recognize the council. The Emperor Maximilian was never more than a lukewarm adherent to it. And even in France there was a striking lack of enthusiasm for it among the clergy. Indeed, there were so few ecclesiastics willing to risk coming to its first session that the opening had to be postponed for several months. The pope's countermeasures had already alienated more than half the cardinals who had originally sanctioned the council. The Italian clergy almost wholly abstained from it. A few representatives finally met for the opening session in the fall of 1511 in Pisa. It was obviously no more than a "rump" assembly even from the beginning and met with the most obvious hostility from the townspeople. For example, the official document or "constitution" proclaiming the opening of the council had to be witnessed: "The whole city was searched in vain for two citizens to act as witnesses; none would consent to officiate, and two unknown persons had to be taken," Pastor, *op. cit.,* VI, 390. The shrewd Machiavelli commented on the same point. See Pasquale Villari, *The Life and Times of Niccolo Machiavelli,* tr. Linda Villari (New York: Charles Scribner's Sons, 1929), I, 493-94. After a few desultory meetings in which vague and general proclamations were made and procedural matters argued, the council was forced to move to Milan under French military protection. Even there popular hostility mounted and the remaining members of the council gradually slipped away. There was a temporary revival of hope and arrogance with the French victory at Ravenna early in 1512 but this hope quickly faded. With the subsequent collapse of the French cause in Italy, the Council of Pisa withered entirely, having taken not one serious step in the direction of genuine reform.

82. This sketch of the Fifth Lateran Council is as distorted and incorrect as is that of the Council of Pisa (n. 81 above). Part of the contrast here is, no doubt, the result of the demands of literary art, as well as of Erasmus' polemical purpose. No such clear contrast actually existed. As far as reform was concerned, the Lateran Coun-

cil was no improvement over the Council of Pisa. It simply had the virtue of legitimacy. The pope's intention was, first of all, tactical and political. He would probably have allowed the council to go on into the area of reform had he lived. (See n. 73 above.) Certainly many members of the council held high hopes for reform. The remarks in the text about the dilatory procedure are simply a hostile view of the usual slow and cumbrous progress of such meetings. Much effort was expended and many documents drawn against the claims of the "schismatic" cardinals. The third session, like the others, did indeed record another denunciation of the "false council," as well as a formal bull laying France under interdict. Negotiations with Henry VIII of England and Ferdinand of Aragon had long since secured their adherence and an open invitation had been extended to the "Princes of Christendom." See the full and detailed report of the council, session by session, in Pastor, *op. cit.,* VI, 406-28.

83. The three cardinals involved were the Spaniard Carvajal, the Venetian Sanseverino, and the Frenchman Briçonnet—the last holdouts among the group. They now resided in France in exile, having been previously stripped of their estates and dignities.

84. This is roughly equivalent to our proverb, "Let sleeping dogs lie." It appears in the *Adagia,* Erasmus, *Opera Omnia,* II, 51 D, item LXIV. The reference is to Vergil's *Aeneid,* III, 699-702, "far off appears Camarina, forbidden forever by oracles to move. . . ."

85. The wars had indeed already been long, stretching back to 1494 and the ill-starred Italian invasion of Charles VIII. From the point of vantage of 1513 or 1514 it must have looked as if the French were exhausted with the loss of Louis XII's advantage in Italy. In fact, the misfortunes of that king were to be no more than an interlude in the French wars for Italy, which were to stretch into the reign of his successor Francis I and beyond. See the standard accounts in Ernest Lavisse, *Histoire de France,* Vol. V, *Les Guerres d'Italie . . .* (Paris: Hachette, 1903), part 1, *passim;* Henri Hauser and Augustin Renaudet, *Les Débuts de l'Age moderne* (Paris: Presses Universitaires de France, 1956), pp. 74 ff, 376 ff; and *The New Cambridge Modern History,* I, Ch. XII, pp. 343-67.

86. The English had become involved in the tangle of continental affairs only in a limited way. Henry VIII, following the lead of Ferdinand of Aragon, his artful father-in-law, had adhered to the papal alliance of the Holy League in 1511, had supported the pope's

ecclesiastical position and the Lateran Council, and was making bellicose overtures to the French. See A. F. Pollard, *Henry VIII* (London *et al.*: Longmans, Green and Co., 1951), pp. 34 ff and G. R. Elton, *England under the Tudors* (London: Putnam, 1954), pp. 70 ff. The specific phrase "mountains of gold" Erasmus had already used with regard to his now tarnished hopes for financial reward in England. See Allen, *Ep. Eras.*, I, Ep. 266, p. 519.

87. It was not so much honor as bribery. The title was conferred upon Louis XI by Pope Paul II during the course of Louis' long conflict with the papacy leading to the Concordat of Ambroise (1472) and dealing with the question of lay jurisdiction in ecclesiastical cases. Despite the honorific title, Louis XI was not noticeably moved. The title subsequently became customary for the French kings.

88. Cf. *Adagia*, Erasmus, *Opera Omnia*, II, 633 A, item LXXX. The reference is to Plautus, *Pseudolus*, I, 2, 8, "You'd sooner leave wolves to guard the sheep than these fellows to watch your home."

89. Referring to the abortive attempt to bring together once more the Greek and Latin churches at the Council of Ferrara-Florence in 1438-39. Important as this council was for the Florentine "Greek Renaissance," the act of union was never accepted by the Greek church. It served only to provide a "paper" victory for the papacy to claim.

90. See n. 5, n. 25, and n. 35 above. Such financial abuses as listed here—the indulgences, dispensations, and the like—were the favorite targets of Julius' many critics; and clearly the most conspicuous category of ecclesiastical abuses during his pontificate. Pastor, *op. cit.*, VI 224-25, states the case thus: "Some of the means which he adopted for the replenishment of his treasury were of a very objectionable kind. His subjects were certainly not oppressed with taxation, but it cannot be denied that he not only sold offices, but also benefices. This formed a serious hindrance to the reform which was so much needed; for if that were carried out, it would mean the abolition of all such sales. It is true that under Julius II the money was employed for the interests of the Church, and not for the enrichment of his family; but this is no justification for persistence in simony. The complaints of contemporaries both in Italy and abroad show how strongly this abuse was resented. Another great evil was that grants of occasional Indulgences were so often employed as a means of obtaining money. In the case of the Jubilee Indulgences, powers for which were conceded by the Pope to

the German Orders, the Chapter of Constance, and the Augsburg Dominicans, the half of the proceeds were to be handed over to Rome. . . . The Pope's fixed income in the year 1510 was estimated by the Venetian Ambassador at 200,000 ducats, and his floating income at 150,000, a very small sum for one in the position of Head of the Church. The accounts of the treasure in the Castel of St. Angelo during the reign of Julius II are of such a nature that it is impossible to arrive at any certain conclusion as to the exact amount; but we know that at his death it was more than had been left by any previous Pope since John XXII." (See n. 35 above.)

91. Cf. *Adagia,* Erasmus, *Opera Omnia,* II, 142 A, item LXXX, the reference "coelum terrae miscendum." It is cited from Suetonius, *Vita Neronis,* "Me mortuo conflagret humus incendiis." Cicero and Quintilian are also cited.

92. The genealogy of this characterization leads back, in all probability, to Tacitus' idealized account of the Germans. See *Germania,* Loeb edition, 5, pp. 270-71. Erasmus had reason to know from bitter experience that the love of money was "radix omnium malorum," for Italian and barbarian alike. He apparently likes the contrast here and cannot resist a jibe at the grasping Italians, especially the clergy.

93. The reputation of the Germans for drunkenness need not be traced to Tacitus, though it may be. This was part of the late medieval-early modern stereotype of the German, abundantly documented. Erasmus specifically dealt with it, as well as with the general boorishness of the Germans, in his colloquy *Inns (Diversoria).* See Craig R. Thompson (trans.), *The Colloquies of Erasmus* (Chicago and London: The University of Chicago Press, 1965), pp. 147-52.

94. While this might have been true at the beginning of the high Middle Ages it would hardly be true in the sixteenth century. Again Erasmus is distorting for emphasis. By this time the great corporate and family banking houses of the north—the Fuggers and Welsers most prominently—having learned the techniques of the Bardi, Peruzzi, and the Medici, had virtually usurped their usurious monopoly.

95. Cast as a reference to wide-spread homosexuality in Italy, this is probably also directed at Julius.

96. Like the love of money, the sale of ecclesiastical offices was by no means an Italian or Roman monopoly. If a contrast existed it was one only of magnitude and opportunity, not of inclination. One can compare the spectacular career of Albrecht, Archbishop of Mainz, with even the most corrupt Italian clergy.

97. This is probably a reference to the storm of anti-papal propaganda. See the discussion of this in the introduction, pp. 25-27.

98. This criticism both of the pope and the secular princes is typical of the moral judgments of Erasmus on this subject. The *locus classicus* in his work is probably *The Praise of Folly,* Dean trans., pp. 107-8. The hypocrisy of gifts, honorary titles, and the like is well documented in this age of the secularized church. Julius simply employed his spiritual powers more openly and more effectively than most of his immediate predecessors, for political advantage. In 1504 he conferred the Golden Rose upon the Republic of Genoa and at Christmas 1505, sent a consecrated sword to Louis XII. See Rodocanachi, *op. cit.,* p. 62. Note also the skillful insertion here of another charge of sexual irregularity against Julius.

99. Cf. *Adagia,* Erasmus, *Opera Omnia,* II, 300 A, item XCVI, referring to the folk belief that mules groomed each other with their teeth and thus making a proverb signifying wicked and infamous people deluding and justifying themselves to each other.

100. The key to this whole passage is not the fact of Julius' intriguing with or against one or another power but the purpose behind his intrigues—the political integrity of Italy and the Papal States. All the powers whose policies involved Italy were the concern of Julius— none more than France and Venice. Of all the Italian states, Venice represented the clearest threat to the States of the Church (see n. 57 above) and Julius turned the weapons of his diplomacy first against Venice, using the French as "a nail to drive a nail." In the spring of 1504, Julius approached both Louis XII of France and the Emperor Maximilian with the proposal of a league against Venice. Both France and the Empire had found their Italian plans blocked by Venice. Differences between Maximilian and the French, however, prevented the league from finally being formed. But the threat was not lost upon Venice, which made some concessions of territory to Julius and promised neutrality in Julius' coming attack on Bologna. At the same time he retained the cooperation of France, which still cherished hopes of an eventual assault upon Venice in concert with the pope. These hopes held the French sufficiently in line for Julius to proceed effectively against Bologna (see n. 57 above).

101. The emperor, after having withdrawn from the league with the pope and the French against Venice four years before, did become a party to the League of Cambrai in 1508, as the text observes, "since he had no other hope of recovering from the Venetians what they

held." He had already been soundly beaten by them in an attempt at unilateral penetration and had been forced to a humiliating three-year truce. The secret articles of the League of Cambrai promised the restoration to Maximilian of the Italian cities Venice had seized from the Empire: Roverdo, Verona, Padua, Vicenza, Treviso, and Friuli.

102. The parties to the League of Cambrai began to move against Venice in the spring of 1509, with great success. The lion's share of the victory went to the French, who defeated the Venetians at Agnadello, May 14, 1509. This was exactly what Julius had feared and, while he did take advantage of the French victory to consolidate his own position in the Romagna, he looked now for some way to counter the French, whose victory had strengthened them out of all proportion. In part, he looked to the now chastened Venetians, but also to the Spanish king Ferdinand. That sly and cautious monarch had watched the proceedings in northern Italy with great interest. While he had no illusions about Julius II, he shared with the pope his fear of the French in Italy, for if they were unchecked in the north, his own interests in Naples might eventually be threatened once more. Thus, Ferdinand was amenable to the pope's proposal for a league to drive the French out of Italy and in the autumn of 1511 joined Julius and Venice in the Holy League.

103. Erasmus here has the intricate time sequence somewhat confused. The pope's reconciliation with Venice came before his rapprochement with Ferdinand. Indeed, this reconciliation had been the reason for the bitterness of the French which necessitated the formation of the Holy League. The French victories under the League of Cambrai had forced Venice to sue and she turned to the pope. Reluctant as he was to be reconciled with that arrogant republic, he had no real choice but to do so or face the worse alternative of a French preponderance in Italy. As agreement was reached between Julius II and Venice early in 1510, the tough old pope gouged every concession possible from his humbled enemy. Venice withdrew her support for a general council; she admitted the right of the pope to pronounce ecclesiastical censure; admitted clerical immunity from taxation, the jurisdiction of ecclesiastical courts, clerical rights to appointment to benefices; she renounced all interference in Ferrara and granted free navigation of the Adriatic to all papal subjects; repudiated all treaties with cities belonging to or claimed by the pope; promised to cease protecting rebels against the church; and to restore all goods taken

from religious associations. For these terms see Pastor, *op. cit.,* p. 319. As one can readily imagine, such treatment did not endear Julius to the Venetians and, even as they swore their loyalty to the pope, they were already looking to the next chance to betray him. See the extended discussion in Federico Seneca, *Venezia e Papa Giulio II* (Padova: Liviana, 1962), p. 144 ff.

104. It was no great trick to detach the emperor from his French alliance in the League of Cambrai. He had always been a weak and reluctant adherent. He had also had disastrous luck against the Venetians and realized, in spite of his pretensions, that he had to go either with the French or the pope. Given the strong position of the French in northern Italy, he could be counted on eventually to stay with Julius. When the Holy League was arranged, the way was left open for Maximilian to join it. While he did not formally avail himself of the alliance, the pope was able to induce him to negotiate a ten-month truce with Venice and thus rob the French of any help he might give them. He allowed the Swiss allies of the pope to pass through his lands to strategic positions in northern Italy and recalled the German mercenaries who were the backbone of the French forces in Italy. Thus Maximilian was persuaded to contribute to the French collapse in Italy and to the diplomatic triumph of the pope.

105. This was a part of the bitter legacy of the Hundred Years War during which the Scots made common cause with France, rightly figuring that an England harried abroad would be less troublesome to her northern neighbor. The Franco-Scottish relationship thus established continued sporadically into the late fifteenth and sixteenth centuries; and was not broken even by the marriage of Henry VII's daughter Margaret to Scotland's James IV. Henry VIII's adherence to the Holy League against France brought trouble with Scotland again. When Henry invaded France in the summer of 1513, the Scots responded by invading England. This threat was ended by the Scots' defeat at Flodden Field and the death there of James IV and the subsequent peace with both Scotland and France. Erasmus was poignantly aware of this, for his pupil and companion in Italy, the natural son of James IV, was killed in the battle. See his account in the bitter diatribe against war in the adage "Spartam nactus es, hanc orna," in Margaret M. Phillips, *The 'Adages' of Erasmus,* pp. 305-8.

106. This refers to the outburst of relief in England at the death of Henry VII in 1509. Erasmus had been summoned back to England

137

from Italy on that occasion by the enthusiastic letters of his English friends presaging an age of gold under the new scholar-king Henry VIII. Erasmus knew something of the harshness of the old king: he had fallen afoul of Henry's fiscal legislation and had had some money confiscated as he left England in 1500 after his first visit there. See Allen, *Ep. Eras.,* I, Ep. 145, p. 343 and I, p. 6. But more than that, several of his closest friends, notably Thomas More, had been in great peril from the mounting tyranny of Henry's last years. See the several contemporary or near contemporary More biographies, e.g. William Roper, *Life of Thomas More* . . . (London: W. Scott, 1890), pp. 5-6.

107. This passage implies an intimate knowledge of the image of young Henry VIII in the first years of his reign, an image of which Erasmus was well aware from his close personal connections with the court. Henry's lust for fame and his juvenile design to recapture the English glory of the Hundred Years War were well known. The Spanish connection had come through the dynastic marriage which Henry VII had arranged with Catherine of Aragon, daughter of Ferdinand and Isabella, first to his eldest son and heir, Prince Arthur and, upon the death of Arthur, to the younger son Henry. Because of the diplomatic wire-pulling of Ferdinand, this marriage connection became an important element in continental politics and a major factor in drawing England into the alliance against France.

108. This statement is based, once more, upon Erasmus' assumption throughout that Julius was the chief architect of the League of Cambrai. As we have seen, n. 34 above, it was largely the doing of France and the Empire and was joined by Julius only at the last moment and with some trepidation. In their effort to box Venice in completely, the chief signatories had solicited all the powers whose borders or interests were in the least threatened by Venice. This was the connection with the King of Hungary, Vladislas II, who came into the league on the hope of regaining territories lost to Venice in Dalmatia and Croatia. When the pope broke with the League of Cambrai he approached Ferdinand of Aragon as a party to his Holy League and Ferdinand agreed. It is in this connection that the text mentions the King of Portugal who, while an ally of Ferdinand, had no particular connection with Julius and the Holy League, certainly no direct connection. As to the Duke of Burgundy "the peer of kings," he was a powerless eight-year-old boy, the Archduke Charles, the

future Emperor Charles V. He was the heir apparent but such policies as the turbulent Netherlands had were dictated largely by Margaret of Austria, Charles' aunt and local regent, and controlled not by European considerations—certainly not Italian—but by strictly local demands. Burgundy played little or no part in implementing the League of Cambrai or the league which succeeded it. While it may seem strange that Erasmus, a Dutchman, should have been so ill-informed about his own country, one must remember that he had done no more than pass through the country for more than ten years and that he felt no strong interest in it at this or any other time.

109. Spain's intervention was induced neither by the threats nor blandishments of the pope but by the self-interest of Ferdinand. The Spanish adherence must be explained almost entirely in those terms. Since his successes in Naples, Ferdinand had no longer a pressing reason for hostility to France. Indeed, the year before Cambrai Ferdinand and Louis XII had had cordial talks at Savona. When Louis and Maximilian joined forces against Venice in the League of Cambrai, Ferdinand had no reason to stand aloof from the league and every reason to come in. After all, he had his own dynastic interests in Italy to protect. Thus Ferdinand became a party to the league. When, as he had foreseen, the jealous allies began to turn on France and the Holy League was formed, he just as easily joined it. He had protected his interests in Italy and now he saw a chance to extend his interests in Spain at the expense of France, and he turned to the project, so long dear to him, of conquering the French-dominated Kingdom of Navarre and realizing the "natural frontiers" of Spain on the north.

110. The Emperor had been bound to neither the French nor Julius "by very great favors." Indeed, he had lost to them both at every turn and they had repeatedly sold him out. Maximilian intrigued for a lifetime in Italy and gained not a foot of territory.

111. The Gelderlanders and their duke Charles of Egmont were indeed the most implacable enemies of Maximilian and his dynasty in the Low Countries. It is difficult to tell where Erasmus' sympathies lay here, if with either side. The hostilities between Egmont and the Hapsburgs continue through this whole period and were not much affected by the succession either of Philip le Bel or the Archduke Charles. Philip, the son of Maximilian and Mary of Burgundy, was generally accepted as the *Prince naturel* by the parties and the estates

of Burgundy, who were more than happy to be rid of Maximilian as regent. There was even greater enthusiasm, after Philip's death, for the young Charles—by all but Egmont, who continued to oppose the "foreigners." Under the circumstances the references to Maximilian's "inciting war" against Gelderland is somewhat obscure. Perhaps, as in n. 108 above, such misinformation is to be explained by Erasmus' unfamiliarity with the affairs of his native land.

112. The references here are to the famed martyrdom of St. Thomas à Becket, which grew out of the controversy between England's Henry II and the papacy; and to the several pieces of anti-papal legislation—such as the Constitutions of Clarendon, the Statute of Provisors, and the Statute of Praemunire in medieval English history, "the Constitutions of their kings of long ago."

113. The young Henry VIII, in response to the promptings of his father-in-law Ferdinand and to his own zeal for glory, had joined the alliance against France and was preparing for an invasion. Erasmus was kept informed of Henry's moves largely by Ammonio's stream of letters. See introduction, pp. 20-22.

114. Erasmus had reason to know about the Donation of Constantine and particularly about its being revealed as a forgery by the Italian humanist Lorenzo Valla. Even before he left his monastery he had "discovered" Valla and was much impressed with him. It was not, however, until the spring of 1505, in Paris, that he published his edition of Valla's *Adnotationes* on the New Testament. See Allen, *Ep. Eras.,* I, p. 99; I, Ep. 182, pp. 407-12,, the epistolary preface to the work. The specific reference here is to a spurious section of Gratian's *Decretum.*

115. R. H. Bainton, *op. cit.,* pp. 4-5, points out the striking similarity of this and the following passage to one in Erasmus' Paraphrases on Mark 2 of 1523, where the lowly Jesus, entering Jerusalem riding on an ass, is contrasted with the Jewish high priest: "No reader could ever mistake the likeness of Julius II." The passage describes, moreover, the pomp, rich ornaments and vestments of the priest, his beetling brows and insolent mouth, and the trains of wagons and mules, noble youths, guards, and trumpeters.

116. This is almost certainly a reference to the stock comic character of Plautus' *Miles Gloriosus,* with an ironic touch added in the superlative "gloriosissime miles."

117. Acts 5:15.

118. Luke 9:1.

119. Acts 9:36-41.

120. Acts 5:1-10.

121. Matt. 5:11-12.

122. II Corinth. 11:23-27.

123. There is a closely parallel passage in the famous adage "Sileni Alcibiadis." See the translation in Margaret M. Phillips, *The 'Adages' of Erasmus,* pp. 281-82. For the Latin see Erasmus, *Opera Omnia,* II, 778 E, Chil. III, Cent. III, Prov. I.

124. Aristotle, *Politics,* VII, 1.

125. The date of Julius' birth is uncertain because of the general obscurity surrounding his early life. Brosch, *op. cit.,* p. 3, accepts the date 1443. But Rodocanachi, *op. cit.,* p. 3, n. 1, concludes that the date 1441 seems the most probable.

126. "Aquam igni miscere," in *Adagia,* Erasmus, *Opera Omnia,* II, 1023 D, item XCIV.

127. Erasmus, during his brief stay in Rome, had personal knowledge of this sort of fulsome court rhetoric. See introduction, n. 51. In part at least, his scathing dialogue *Ciceronianus* was directed against it. He mentions several of these "Apologists" by name and tells a famous story of one whom he doesn't name, addressing a formal declamation to Julius: "An introduction and a peroration longer nearly than the declamation itself were devoted to singing the praises of Julius whom he called Jupiter Optimus Maximus and who, holding and rattling the thunder and lightning in his all powerful right hand, could do whatever he wanted through fear alone," Erasmus, *Opera Omnia, Ciceronianus,* I. 993 A. Cf. the dialogue, ll. 244-45.

128. Matt. 5:13; Mark 9:49; Luke 14:34.

129. Julius was indeed "a great builder," the greatest among the Renaissance popes. The Rome of the Renaissance was virtually created by him, including the beginning of the present cathedral of St. Peter. His commission of his own monumental tomb and the decoration of the Sistine Chapel are well known. See the complete story of his artistic patronage and artistic and architectural accomplishments in Klaczko, *op. cit.* and De Tolnay, *op. cit.*

WESTMAR COLLEGE LIBRARY